The Cloth Dollmaker's Source Book

A guide to the best in mail order
for cloth doll & soft toy making . . .
patterns, kits, etc.

ANNE PATTERSON DEE

BETTERWAY PUBLICATIONS, INC. White Hall, Virginia

Published by Betterway Publications, Inc.
White Hall, VA 22987

Book design by Diane Nelson
Cover photograph by Erin Garvey
Typography by East Coast Typography, Inc.

Library of Congress Cataloging in Publication Data

Dee, Anne Patterson.
    The cloth dollmaker's source book.

    Includes index.
    1. Dollmaking — Equipment and supplies — Directories.
2. Soft toy making — Equipment and supplies — Directories.
3. Dolls — Catalogs.   4. Soft toys — Catalogs.
I. Title.
TT175.D44   1985   745.592'21   85-13460
ISBN 0-932620-52-3 (pbk.)

Printed in the United States of America

0 9 8 7 6 5 4 3 2 1

Dedicated
in loving memory
of
RUTH HAZEL HENDERSON
1946-1971
who enriched a decade of my life

Table of Contents

Acknowledgements

Dolls Shown on the Cover Are:

1. *TinyTown Kids™ by Cabbie Glass, courtesy of Ms. G's Softworks.*

2. *Rita Doll by Virginia Robertson, courtesy of Osage County Quilt Factory.*

3. *Victorian Doll by Elinor Peace Bailey, courtesy of Little Old Lady Originals.*

4. *Mohlee by Loretta Daum Byrne, courtesy of Little Lotus.*

5. *Bears and llama by Diane Babb, courtesy of By Diane.*

6. *Farmer in the Dell and his Wife, courtesy of Dorothy Everds of Miss Perky's Patterns.*

7. *RicRac raccoon courtesy of Pauli Crandall of Pauliwog.*

About the Author

Anne Patterson Dee graduated from the University of Texas at Austin in 1968 with a B.J. degree in Magazine Editing and Layout. She worked as a feature writer for the daily *Austin-American Statesman* newspaper before moving to the Chicago area with her husband, a classics professor and department chairman at the University of Illinois. She is the owner of Daedalus Publications, Inc. and the editor of *CraftsWoman*, a bimonthly marketing magazine for home-based craftswomen, needlecrafters and designers. She has written several booklets on selling crafts. *The Cloth Dollmaker's Source Book* is her first full-length book.

Introduction

I once had a sweet little doll, dears,
The prettiest doll in the world;
Her cheeks were so red and so white, dears,
And her hair was so charmingly curled.

Charles Kingsley, *The Water Babies*

The old-fashioned rag doll, made of little more than everyday materials and a lot of love, has intrigued me since the 1970s when I bought a small fully-jointed cloth doll, with a red and yellow cotton print dress and black yarn curls, at a mall craft fair in Milwaukee. I assume I originally picked her out as a gift for a child, but she is still mine. My mother has admired her on several occasions, but I haven't parted with the doll yet. Even earlier, I remember liking a patchwork hippo and an Appalachian doll enough to receive them later as gifts from various family members.

Cloth doll and soft animal designs have proliferated so much in the past decade that there is now a marvelous variety available. Thousands of patterns are available and most of them can be ordered through the mail. The three women who I see as forerunners of good design in the mail-order cloth doll pattern business - Colette Wolff of Platypus, Carolee Luppino of Carolee Creations and Loretta Daum Byrne of Little Lotus - have been joined by hundreds of others. All these creative minds mean a bigger selection for you. Information on more than 300 designers and *thousands* of patterns is included in this source book. The secret to using this guide fully is simple: the catalogs these companies offer will lead you to still other designs. Carolee, e.g., has 75 different dolls, but there was room to show only a few.

For those of you who, like me, admire cloth dolls but don't have time to make them, I've included two chapters featuring handmade dolls, animals and bears. It's easy to buy excellent quality handcrafted items through the mail. As common as craft fairs are these days, they do come and go in a weekend.

The numerous marketing tips in this book are presented in good faith to assist dollmakers and doll designers who plan to start or who already have started doll-related businesses. While the information has been researched and prepared with great care, it is not the business of the author, the publisher or the women quoted within to render professional services regarding the legal, taxation or accounting aspects of marketing. Readers are asked to exercise normal good judgment in determining when the services of a lawyer or other professional would be appropriate to their needs.

The information contained in this book is based on research and materials provided by those mentioned; every effort has been made to insure accuracy, but neither the author nor Betterway Publications, Inc. assumes any liability in cases of error or changing circumstances. Any business relations or other activities undertaken as a result of information contained herein, or any claims arising therefrom, are the responsibilities of the parties involved and not of the author or Betterway Publications, Inc.

 NOTE TO READERS

There will be another book on this subject and I want to make sure that it will contain updated information and new sources, as well as those inevitably left out of this edition. If you design or make your own cloth dolls, animals or bears or have related supplies, materials or publications, please contact me to receive a questionnaire for possible inclusion in related books or a second edition of this book. As the publisher of *Crafts Woman*, a marketing magazine for homebased craftswomen, needlecrafters and designers, I am always interested in hearing from those of you who own small dollmaking businesses. We like to feature articles on this subject from time to time. And, of course, I would love to hear your comments about this book and your dealings with any of the companies listed.

Happy dollmaking!

Write to: Anne Patterson Dee
             The Cloth Dollmaker's Source Book
             P.O. Box 848
             Libertyville, IL 60048-0848

How to Use This Book

Most of the companies listed in this book will send you additional literature about their products. It's always a good idea when inquiring to send an SASE (self-addressed, stamped envelope) since many of these mail-order businesses are home-based and do not have large budgets. But if the cost of a catalog is given, simply send the amount indicated.

If you are looking for a specific design, product, or maker, start with the index. There are 1312 entries, listing companies, business owners, patterns, materials, supplies, accessories, publications, and handmade dolls and animals. Many of the doll designers simply give "personal" names for their dolls, so it is sometimes difficult to know what kind of doll is meant. *The Cloth Dollmakers' Source Book* is meant to point you in the right direction, bringing cloth doll and soft animal designers from across the country to your attention.

What child in me peeks round the room
To see the doll beneath the tree.
All I am is required not to snatch her to me
    and away from my little one.
Thus deprived, I stitch them,
Because no one can then ask questions like —
"Are you playing with dolls?"
"Aren't you a little old for that?"
Or worse and worse, "How can you waste your time so?"
No, now they will leave me alone,
And never know
That my child within revels in the fantasy
That I have made a world that has no pain.
A world that you and I can clearly understand.

                              elinor peace bailey '85

CHAPTER 1

Cloth Doll Patterns & Kits

A cloth doll can be a soft and cuddly plaything for a child or a sculptured art figure that only an adult can fully appreciate. This section contains information on 109 companies - most of them homebased - that offer cloth doll patterns and/or kits. The designs available include baby dolls, toddlers and kids, costume dolls and character dolls, sock dolls and silk-screened dolls, fashion dolls and fairy tale dolls, puppet dolls and pillow dolls, two-faced dolls and topsy-turvy dolls, plain and simple Amish dolls and elaborately dressed Victorian dolls, knitted dolls and crocheted dolls and dolls made out of cotton, muslin, felt, polyknit and nylon hose. Many of these companies also offer bear and/or animal patterns and some have supplies as well.

ALICE'S DOLLS

Alice Pattinson
PO Box 176
Gillette, WY 82716-0017
307/682-9716

Established in 1974
Brochure: $1

24" Miss Pat; 14" Baby Piper and Blanket; 22" Luke the Scarecrow; 20" Tedee Pat; 20" and 26" Dalee O! The Uptown Clown and 20" Willie O! The Downtown Clown; 17" Sisse Brown Eyes and wardrobe; 18 other designs.

When Alice agreed to make a rag doll for her neighbor's little girl, she had no idea she was about to launch a business that would bring her "thousands of new friends from all over the world." That first doll, made of pink gingham, was such a success that friends and neighbors began asking for the pattern. Today Alice has ten scrapbooks filled with letters, newspaper articles and photos. She recently appeared on a national cable television series where she demonstrated how to make "Miss Pat", her first and most popular doll.

Alice Pattinson and a few of her creations.

ALL DOLLED UP

Sandra J. Hathaway
303 Kohr Road
Kings Park, NY 11754-1215
516/269-9074

Brochure: Free with SASE

15", 20" and 25" basic cloth doll pattern; overalls and doll dress pattern; 9" doll with wardrobe; Hairlooms, for making looped yarn doll hair.

AMITY PUBLICATIONS

Suzy Lawson
78688 Sears Road
Cottage Grove, OR 97424-9470
503/942-7501

Established in 1981
Catalog: $1

21" Amish Girl with dress, apron, hat, pants and 22"x22" quilt; 21" Amish Boy with shirt, trousers, suspenders, felt hat and 5"x7" felt puppy.

Because of the biblical injunction (Deuteronomy 5:8), "Thou shalt not make thee any graven image . . .", Amish dolls were traditionally made without faces. The clothing, colors and bare feet of these dolls reflect the image of the young children in old order Amish communities.

ANDEE'S ARTI-FACTS

Andrea W. Warner
1641 N. Mary Dr.
Santa Maria, CA 93454-1635
805/928-3996

Established in 1980
Information: $1 and LSASE
(refundable)

3" to 6' dolls, including 8" Micro Tot dolls; 10" and 15" doll caddies.

 ANDEE'S MARKETING TIPS

Don't overlook unusual markets. If you make well-constructed, washable dolls, bears or soft animals, contact pediatricians, clinics or the pediatric ward at your local hospital. Offer to donate a few items in exchange for a posted notice telling people how to contact you and/or that your dolls are available at the hospital's gift shop. Parents love to buy toys that comfort their sick or scared child. A hospital donation is also good for free newspaper publicity.

ANNEMADE

953 W. 3rd St.
Pomona, CA 91766-1420

Brochure: $1.25

8" Video Babes.

Kay Davis and members of her Puff Family.

ATLANTA PUFFECTIONS

Kay Davis
PO Box 13524
Atlanta, GA 30324-0524
404/233-0673

Established in 1982
Catalog: $.50 and LSASE

3" to 10" Puff family, including angels, astronauts, mini angel, bride, groom, attendants, mom and baby, Mrs. Santa, Santa, black-eyed Susan and doll, papa gnome and baby, mama gnome and baby, mini gnomes, chef, super girl and boy, ball players, potpourri Puff; 2 1/2" to 6" Puff animal friends, including Christmas mouse, frog, pig, bunny, papa mouse, mama mouse, Missy Mouse, mice children, papa bear, mama bear; 3" to 4 1/2" Christmas tree ornaments, including mouse in stocking, miniature lamb, Missy Mouse, mouse in nutshell; 10" Puff Snowflake, top-of-the-tree angel; 3" eyelet angel; 10" baby carriage; 8" mom and baby; 5" Plumpkins; glue sticks; glue gun; pearl button beads; curly chenille; black bead eyes (3mm to 10mm).

Kay made her first dress when she was ten, but she has always hated to cook. "When a close friend who hates to sew offered to cook in exchange for my crafts, my first 'business' was born," she says. This developed into an annual Christmas bazaar held in her home for nine years, but the bazaar was so successful it caused its own demise by outgrowing her house. So Kay began selling her creations at regional craft shows where she decided it was important to offer crafts with wide audience appeal, in large quantities and with minimal cost for materials. Unlike many cloth doll designers, Kay encourages her customers to sell her designs at craft fairs where they have proven to be good sellers. Her Puff dolls can be made out of most fabrics and can be glued instead of stitched for fast production.

BABES & BEARS

Christine Lawrence
PO Box 311
North San Juan, CA 95960-0311
916/292-3773

Established in 1983
Brochure with color photo: $1

22" Gopal, mythical character doll.

 CHRISTINE'S MARKETING TIPS

Be as creative and courageous selling your patterns and hand-made products as you were when you designed them. Don't be put off by people who don't appreciate your enthusiasm. Have some inexpensive cards printed and put them in every conceivable place that women who sew and/or have some relationship with children might go - laundromats, fabric stores, bulletin boards.

BARONCHELLI DOLLS
& DOLL PATTERNS

Consuelo Garcia and
Sandra Mellon
51 Windward Dr.
Barnegat, NJ 08005-1853
609/698-6835

Established in 1983

11" Cobbler Doll; 9 1/2" Faerie Elves Imp and Blink; handmade felt dolls.

Consuelo, better known as Chelo, is a graduate of the Mayer School of Design in New York City where she majored in pattern making. She has worked in the clothing industry for more than 25 years and began making dolls in 1980. Her doll library has more than 500 books. "I am consumed by the need to learn all I can about the art of dollmaking," she explains. "My great inspirations are Kathe Kruse, Izannah Walker and Madam Lenci. Their great legacy to the world of dolls is priceless."

Consuelo Garcia of Baronchelli Dolls

BAYBERRY

Janet K. Rostocki
PO Box 24404
Dayton, OH 45424-0404

Established in 1984
Color brochure: $1

24" Sugarlumps with clothes; 14" Pinkle Winkle, upside-down doll; plastic wig winder.

Pinkle Winkle and Sugarlumps, © Bayberry

BEARS AND BABES

Cheryl A. Knowles
PO Box 6062
Chillicothe, OH 45601-6062
614/772-1218

Established in 1983
Information and photos: SASE

22" Mary with 2" teddy bear.

Cheryl Knowles and her bears and babes.

BEST FRIENDS

1813 E. 14th St.
The Dalles, OR 97058-3305

10" Anne Angel and Friends, boy or girl angel.

BONNIE ELAINE DOLLS

130 E. Placer St.
Auburn, CA 95603-5242

18", 20" and 22" fully-jointed dolls.

Cobbler Doll by *Consuelo Garcia* © 1984

Baronchelli Patterns
51 Windwood Dr., Barnegat, N.J. 08005

**Cobbler Doll by
Consuelo Garcia**

**11" Doll
(Seated)**

MATERIALS NEEDED:

- 1/3 yd. muslin - 40" wide
- Black cotton fabric:
  6½" long x 16½" wide.
- Soft cotton denim:
  8" long x 12" wide.
- Backed <u>soft</u> vynel:
  7½" long x 8½" wide.
- Scrap of gold felt.
- 1 lb. of polyester Fiberfill
- White fake fur (tiny piece).
- Thread: black, white, red.

- Gesso (available at art supply stores)
- Hair spray
- Elmers glue
- Spray coating - matte finish
- Makeup: Ultima II moisterizing cream on
  concealer & pink lipstick
- Tempera paint -small jars:
  black & beige or tan
- Wood: 3/4" wide for bench
  3/8" diameter dowel
  (see pattern for measurements.)
- Eyeglasses: 2-6" long 28 gauge wires.

DIRECTIONS for Making Eyeglasses:

TRIM

Form eyeglasses by twisting wire around two pencils as shown in diagram
above. Paint them black and varnish when paint is dry.

APRON:

Pin, only if you have to, on edges **A** and **B**.

Mark with tailors chalk - one strip 1" wide x 5½" long. Stitch 3/8"
away from long edge. Stitch 3/8" away from first stitches. Trim close
to stitches. Place the band on top edge of apron 1/2" in. Edge stitch
to hold in place. Stitch 3/8" away from edge of apron.

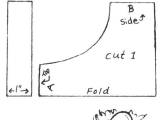

Tack the back at start points:

← start

HAMMER:

To make hammer you will need a small wooden toy clothespin.
Actual size of finished hammer with thin dowel
handle is shown to the right. Cut off one
side of the clothespin to make the head. Sand
it slightly to form a better hammer shape.

Glue to dowel handle. After glue has dried,
stain the wood. Varnish the next day.

cut off →

Actual size

BENCH:

At dots indicated on the bench pattern, drill
3 holes on bottom and 1 hole on top of bench- 3/8" wide.

Glue in dowels. When dry, stain & varnish.

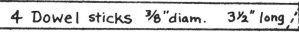

4 Dowel sticks ⅜" diam. 3½" long

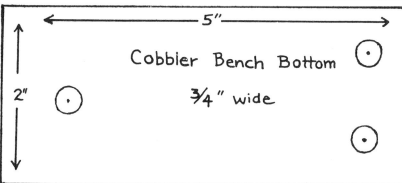

5"

Cobbler Bench Bottom

¾" wide

2"

height: 4 3/4"

Attention to detail creates a masterpiece in this Cobbler Doll by Consuelo Garcia © Baronchelli Patterns

CABIN KIDS

Bonnie Whitcomb and Frankie
Dayton
2347 Wylie
Missoula, MT 59802-3531
406/549-9566

Established in 1985
Brochure: $.50

16" and 18" Baby Ann, My Sweetheart, Judy Jogger, Heather.

Bonnie, the mother of two, and Frankie, the mother of four, have joined forces to market the patterns for their dolls.

CAMILLE DESIGNS

Mary Huber
517 S. Milwaukee St.
Theresa, WI 53091
414/488-5632

Established in 1982
Brochure: $.50

14" and 18" Chuckles the Clown; 7 1/2" Tiny Clown; 5 3/4" Itsy Bitsy Doll; 8" and 18" Rosebud; cradles for 8 1/2" to 18" dolls.

Mary started her pattern business because of a need to keep busy during a very depressing time. Her son was seriously injured in a car accident in 1980 and her mother became totally disabled from a bad fall in 1981. "I took care of her daily for eight months, then decided to take a trip to Montana to visit my daughters. When I returned home, nine days later, the phone rang almost immediately and I was notified that my mother had just died," says Mary. "After this, I kept thinking of ways to avoid my feelings of guilt and grief that seemed to be overwhelming." Mary named the business after her daughter who loves dolls and toys. Chuckles the Clown was designed during the time she cared for her mother.

Clowns by Mary Huber, © Camille Designs

CARLSEN CREATIONS

Ann Carlsen
7 Parker Road
Bedford, MA 01730-2053

Established in 1983
Catalog: $1 (refundable
with first order)

14" When I Grow Up Dolls (police, paramedic, fireman, farmers, doctor, nurse, cowboy, cowgirl, sports figures); 14" Dolls From Around the World (France, West Germany, Netherlands, Sweden, Norway, Denmark, Iceland, Lapland, Scotland, England, Wales, Mexico, Korea, India, Japan); also dolls in colonial, Indian and Eskimo costumes; 6" to 12" Terry Toys (bear, gingerbread man, duck); 14" Cinderella and Prince Charming, Goldilocks and the Three Bears; 14" ethnic Santas; 17" Princess Victoria and wardrobe; 17" June bride and wardrobe; topsy-turvey doll; Pegasus, unicorn, hatching dragon, fairies; bed and bed covers.

 ANN'S MARKETING TIPS

When starting out, classified ads are probably the best bet; the return on display ads is better when you have name recognition. To help encourage initial catalog requests, try offering a small free pattern with the catalog. Until you can project the demand for a pattern, consider having patterns reproduced on a copy machine rather than pay for expensive printing. This is especially helpful when you are first designing the pattern, because you will invariably leave something out. This lets you make changes without throwing out expensive patterns.

© Carlsen Creations.

CAROLEE CREATIONS

Carolee Luppino
787 Industrial Dr.
Elmhurst, IL 60126-1141
312/530-7175

Established in 1971
Color catalog: $1

16" Amy, 18" Katie, 19" May; 72 other designs; body fabrics, including velour (fleshtone), broadcloth (pale peach, warm brown, tan), fleece (pink, fleshtone); yarn (10 colors); fur (10 colors); short fur (3 colors); pre-cut eyepieces; buttons; hair loom; fray check; 3" and 8" needles; doll stands; air soluble pen; pattern tracer.

In 1970, Carolee was a professional volunteer with two grade-school children and a driving urge to *do something*. When she became pregnant with her third child, she decided to sell the patterns for the popular three-dimensional dolls she had made for school and church bazaars. For a total investment of $3.40, she ran her first classified ad in a small publication. "The first few months were very slow with only a few orders a week," recalls Carolee, "but I didn't know enough to be discouraged so I just kept 'plugging away'."

A year later, she invested $100 in an ad in a national magazine. "I nearly drove the editor crazy before I made a commitment. $100 was an awful lot to spend - in fact, it represented all my profits up to that time." The response to the ad encouraged her to buy more small ads in other magazines. "By this time the mail carrier was beginning to look at me a little strangely and we had our first order from overseas."

Carolee ran her first one-third page color ad in the summer of 1975. "Well organized as usual, we were on vacation when the ad came out. I had arranged for a neighbor girl to take in the mail each day and date each bundle so that they could be filled on a first come/first served basis," she says. "When we returned, I found my living room *lined* with grocery bags full of mail for *each* day we were away!"

The rest, as they say, is history. Carolee hired her first part-time employee at that time and the mailman started delivering her mail in his Jeep before he walked the rest of the route. A few years later, he was delivering the mail in trays. In 1980, Carolee's husband, Joe, left his job and joined her. Today, the business has grown to include 21 employees and a leased building in an industrial area west of Chicago - and these days the mailman comes to their office and *picks up* the mail.

 CAROLEE'S MARKETING TIPS

If you are thinking about starting a business, plan to spend the next seven years of your life establishing a unique one. You have to be willing to give up your social life almost entirely if you are serious about making a business succeed. Give your customers the best possible products and service. If your customers are happy, they will *stay* your customers.

May (above)
Katie and Amy. ©*Carolee Creations*

CHARLOTTE LARKIN CREATIONS

Charlotte Larkin
PO Box 3189
Easton, PA 18043-3189

9" to 26" dolls; 8" Little Teddy.

CHERIE'S 3-D CREATIONS

Cherie Jean Brown
Suite 235, 10615-G Tierrasanta
San Diego, CA 92124-2605
619/569-8120

Established in 1984
Brochure: $1.25

19" Peter and Pierre clowns; 19" Honey Tots; Sleepy-Time Baby; 15" Uncle Bill's Bear; 19" Mr. and Mrs. S.; 19" Perfect Gramma and Granpa; 18" Kendra; Doll Pattern Club membership.

© *Cherie's 3-D Creations*

 CHERIE'S MARKETING TIPS

People who buy handmade dolls and soft toys at craft fairs are looking for quality and individuality that they can't find in commercially-made toys. Be sure to use quality materials and sew snaps, buttons and trim securely. Use pleasing color combinations and correctly-proportioned prints. Use pastels for babies, primary colors for toddlers and young children and dark shades and combinations of secondary colors for adult dolls. Make sure your dolls have that *something* that makes them unique and desirable - this could be anything from a mischievous twinkle in the eye to additional wardrobe pieces or accessories.

CLEVER CREATIONS

Tami Lockman
35581 WCR 31
Eaton, CO 80615
303/454-2049

Established in 1979
Brochure: $1

Tami Lockman, Dollmaker

28" Humpty Dumptys (17" when sitting), including Top Hat Boy, Humpty Girl, Country Boy, Santa Claus, Mrs. Santa Claus; handmade Humpty Dumpty dolls.

"I never have been the head of this business," admits Tami. "It does what *it* wants and I work myself to death trying to keep up with it." Initially, all Tami wanted to do was get rid of the surplus scraps of fabric that were left over from various sewing projects. "I used to be the shy, homebody type who had to force myself to get out, mingle with people and *do something*," she says. Now she has learned how to obtain licenses, get copyrights registered, buy supplies wholesale, deals with printers and store buyers, drive a packed station wagon in the Denver traffic, set up for shows and deal with customers. "I feel I'm ready for anything now," says Tami. "I didn't plan on doing all this, but once the ball gets to rolling, you either trot to keep on top or you get squashed everytime it goes around."

Connie Hindmarsh, Dollmaker

CONNIE'S CUTIES INC.

Connie Hindmarsh
2414 Heutte Dr.
Norfolk, VA 23518-4532
804/588-2190

Brochure with color photo:
$1 (refundable)

No-sew 10" Wee Wee; 18" Preemie; 22" New Born; handmade dolls.

Connie spent eleven years performing on children's television, including the writing and production of "Connie's Magic Cottage." She feels that children frequently prefer cloth dolls to more expensive commercial products, so she decided to manufacture her own designs. Today, Connie teaches full-time and devotes evenings, weekends and summers to her mail-order business.

 CONNIE'S MARKETING TIPS

Start out with classified ads. Be careful with display ads; the time of the year you advertise *does* make a difference.

COTTAGE CREATIONS

Carol Anderson and
Kristi Williams
PO Box 108
Cottage Grove, WI 53527-0108
608/839-4841 or
608/839-4758

Established in 1983
Brochure: $.25

14" knitted one-piece Nationality Friends, Sven and Solveig Scandinavian and Bridget and Paddy Irish.

Kristi and Carol believe they have the only all-in-one hand knit seamless doll on the market. "We believe hand knitting is a fiber art that is just beginning a renaissance in this country as people realize the creativity involved in joining various colors and textures of yarn together."

 CAROL'S AND KRISTI'S MARKETING TIPS

The word "earn" can be found in the word "learn". *Learn* if you want to earn $$$. Read everything you can so you can quote what others are doing and evaluate their strong and weak points to make sure there is a spot in the market that needs your product. If you value what you are doing, put some effort and money into developing a good product.

THE COUNTRY COTTAGE

Linda Corrin
1112 Coile Lane
Knoxville, TN 37922-5903
615/691-5345

Established in 1983
Flyer: $1 (refundable)

16" Calico Country and Amish Dolls; 16" jointed teddy bears; cat, duck, pig, trotter, cow, rabbit, geese, sheep.

THE COUNTRY PLACE

Judy Andrew
Rt. 1, Box 40
Gardner, KS 66030-9715

14" to 17" dolls; 13", 18" and 34" Prince and Princess Frogs.

CRAFTS UNLIMITED

Kathleen Havens
1633 Babcock #233
San Antonio, TX 78229-4725
512/436-0984

Established in 1983
Catalog: $1

6" and 13" Whimsical Angel; 6" Leprechaun.

KATHLEEN'S MARKETING TIPS

Keep the QSP principle - Quality, Service, Pricing - in mind and profit should come in the form of re-orders from satisfied customers.

CRAFTY CREATIONS

Vivian Womack
PO Box 867
Clovis, CA 93613-0867
209/431-6312

Established in 1976
Brochure: $.50

14" to 19" dolls; Sleepy-Awake, doll with two faces; 8" and 12" Puf-Kins; Honey Bunny and Family.

CURIOUS CHARACTERS LTD.

Judy and Steve Mahlstedt
2609 S. Blauvelt
Sioux Falls, SD 57105-5118
605/338-6716

Established in 1982
Brochure: SASE

10" Emily, soft-sculpture baby puppet; 20" Amanda, newborn; gnomes and elves; 100% nylon; 3 1/2" needles.

Judy sold 6,000 patterns in the first six months after she placed a full-color display ad in the March 1983 issue of *Crafts*, a national crafts periodical. "I was very lucky," she says. "I have never been 'in the red'." Her initial investment of approximately $2,000 was made back the first month, with 1,200 patterns sold at $4 each. Judy shared eleven marketing tips for novice doll pattern designers in a special issue of *CraftsWoman* magazine published in November 1983. These excellent tips are reprinted here in their entirety, but she would like to add a very strong caution. "Do not invest more than you can afford to lose," she advises. "Most people who try to make it in mail-order do *not* succeed. In many cases, it is not because their product is not a quality product. It is because they are unable to catch the attention of the public. You need to have something that really makes you stand out in the crowd."

JUDY'S MARKETING TIPS

(1) SHOP AROUND ON EVERYTHING! Obviously, you will price printers and advertisers, but did you know that most banks charge a business account to *deposit* checks? I found out after I opened my account that I would pay six to eight cents for each check that I deposited. Since even a small mail-order business can easily deposit 750 to 1,000 checks per month, we are talking about a substantial amount of money. I was able to get around this charge by changing over to checking with interest just before my first ad appeared. Now I pay no service charge, and the bank pays me a fee (interest) each month. By the way, don't expect your banker to suggest this option. I got the advice from one of my competitors.

And that leads us to something I did right. I contacted other designers and asked for advice. Each time I ordered a pattern I liked (for evaluation, as well as for the pleasure of making the doll), I included a note regarding my hope of getting into the business and I usually included a picture of my dolls. I received several friendly responses, invariably from the busiest and most successful, and I got a lot of good advice. One woman seemed to take me on as a personal project and became my mentor. It is thanks to her that I got the courage to go ahead, and with her guidance, I avoided many costly errors.

(2) DISPLAY YOUR PRODUCT AT ITS BEST. One thing my mentor did was to convince me to run my first ad, *Emily*, in color. I had intended to use the less expensive black and white, but her confidence in the doll convinced me to spend the extra dollars and taught me a good lesson in marketing. Always present the product in the best light available. *Emily* would have sold in black and white, but not nearly at the rate she has sold in color. She did so well that I have a cushion to fall back on if one of my newer patterns does not do well. If your item shows much better in color, pay for color.

(3) CONSIDER AN AD AGENCY. Faced with the prospect of running a color ad, I had to admit my ignorance in dealing with the magazine's specifications, so I approached an ad agency for help. This will cost you more, but has certain advantages when you are starting out and have a non-existent credit rating. Magazine ads are placed three or four months in advance of the date of the issue. This means an ad placed in September will appear no earlier than the December issue. Now, the December issue actually comes out in November (don't worry, you'll learn to think in these convoluted terms after a while), so you will have two months to wait until the reader sees what you are selling.

If you follow the advice of most and run two or three ads in succession, you will be placing two ads before the first one comes out. And you will have little time to see a return on the first before you will have to place the third. In the meantime, if you have no credit, the magazine will want their money right away.

This is where the agency, which should have a good credit rating, comes in. The magazine does not bill the agency until the ad comes out. You may even have some money coming in before the agency gets around to billing you for that first ad. (We are assuming the agency will extend you credit, of course.) The agency receives a commission from the magazine, so your only extra expense is for the initial set-up and graphics work, assuming you provide the photo and copy. In my case, going through an agency for the initial ad cost me $100 more.

Having said this, let me caution you to be extremely careful in choosing your advertising agency. I recently spoke with a woman who was being billed twice what we both knew the color separation had cost her ad agency. In addition, the agency insisted that the magazine had refused them credit, and they were demanding payment in advance. My own experience with ad agencies has not been entirely satisfactory and, unless the cash flow advantages outweigh the other considerations, you may wish to deal directly with the magazine you are advertising in.

I left the agency after four months and will do my own ads until it becomes too much of a hassle. The magazines offer advice on setting up ads and many will even do it for you at no extra charge, if you provide them with layout, copy and photos.

(4) KNOW WHEN YOU NEED PROFESSIONAL HELP. It costs me $1 per page to have my instructions typed on an IBM by someone who doesn't have to white out every other letter because of mistakes. Not only does the finished product look neater, but my printer is happier because my paste-up is cleaner.

And speaking of printers, call every shop within a reasonable distance for price quotes, even the ones you don't think can handle the job. The differences in bids are staggering. When you get a good quote, ask for it in writing, and make sure it is for the actual job you are having done. You may want to have your pattern done at one shop and your envelopes done at another.

By law, the printer is allowed to deliver up to a 10% underrun on a job, meaning you can get 900 sheets when you have ordered 1,000 and you must accept that. However, ask your printer if he will guarantee you no underruns. Most will, and you will usually get an overrun. Since you are not going to sit down and count 5,000 sheets of paper when your pattern is delivered, it is important that you find a printer you can trust.

I recently ordered 2,000 brochures from a man who offered colored ink at no extra cost. When I ran out of brochures after sending out 1,600, I decided that my regular printer's charge of $25 for colored ink on a job was not so bad. I didn't lose that much in brochures, but the frustration I felt as I waited for new ones to be printed was far more annoying than the extra money would have been.

(5) CONTROL YOUR EXPENSES. Contrary to what you might think, *printing* is not your biggest expense, even if you have a very detailed pattern, as I do. But you must print a large volume, or printing costs *will* overwhelm you. I was so supremely confident of *Emily's* imminent success that I printed a whole 200 patterns the first time around. My mentor gently advised me *never* to order less than 1,000. She was right. If it is going to go at all, you will sell 1,000 easily. For only twice the cost of 200 patterns, I had 1,000 printed the next time.

If printing isn't your main cost, what is? *Postage* can be a real killer, and you must either charge extra for it or figure it into your price. Since it irritates me to have to tack on that extra at the bottom when I am ordering something, I decided to include it in my price. The first time you write a check to the postoffice for $200 worth of stamps, you will realize that mailing is expensive.

Encourage your customers to send a SASE (self-addressed, stamped envelope) if they want a reply to an inquiry. But for heaven's sake, don't demand it if they are inquiring about a lost order! And be flexible. We all know it is easy to forget the stamp. My printer suggested that I cut down on the size of the type I use, so I now have them reduce my manuscript to 74% of the original pica type-size. (This also makes for a neater look.) You may qualify for a book rate on certain items. Check with your post office.

Advertising, of course, is your largest single expense unless you are hiring employees. Don't go overboard and spread yourself too thin. Research the magazines carefully. Where are your competitors advertising? Which magazines have a healthy looking mail-order ad section? Are ads dropping off in the magazines you are buying? There must be a reason.

Don't fall into the trap of thinking that you are better off advertising where there are no other items like yours. It may be they aren't there because they died there. I would much rather be next to five similar ads so the customer can see why mine is that much better than the others.

I chose to advertise in a magazine that I myself bought and enjoyed. I figured my customers had similar interests and tastes and would also buy that magazine. It turned out that I was right. Don't be in a big rush to get your ads into every magazine in the rack. Try two or three, if you must, but code your ads so you will know where the orders are coming from.

(6) RECORD ORDERS PRECISELY FROM THE START. To code an ad, put a department number into your address. For example, I coded my July 1983 ad in *Crafts* magazine with Dept. C783. Not only does this tell me that I am still getting a good response from this ad now (in September), but it also gives me a clue as to what my customer wants if she says only, "Send me the pattern," because this ad was for *Emily*.

Codes are marvelous sources of information and I use them on my address labels too. As I open the mail, I write the proper code on each order and my typist copies it as the first line of the address. If the previously mentioned order came to me on the 6th of September, Nellie types 90683 C783 E 400. The E tells my envelope stuffer that *Emily* goes into this one. The 400 tells my bookkeeper that this order brought in $4. The 90683 tells us (and Uncle Sam) the date the $4 was received. We keep a carbon of each day's labels as a daily log.

If the post office returns the order, I know exactly which day's original orders to look through to find if we made a mistake in typing the address. If someone writes about an order not received within a reasonable length of time, this code is on the customer card so I know when we processed the order. Right now I am both the envelope stuffer and the bookkeeper, but in the future, these jobs will be done by employees and I can be easily replaced because of our coding. Also, we can all be replaced by a computer at some later date, if need be.

(7) SET PRICES CAREFULLY. Because you will need to replace yourself with "paid" help sooner or later, you must not set your prices so low that you can't afford to pay someone to do what you are doing. Also, a price that is too low can suggest lack of quality, no matter how good your product really is. On the other hand, don't price too high. There is a limit to what your talents are worth. Check the going rate on the patterns you ordered for research. Most of them probably cost less than $.25 to print and if you think in terms of printing as your only expense, a common mistake among beginners, you may wonder how these people dare charge $4 to $5 for this little bit of paper.

Figure every possible cost, now and in the future - printing, advertising, bookkeeping, typing, office supplies, postage, envelopes, labels, etc. There is a lot involved in sending out one little pattern. And remember, if the next one is a bomb, this one has to carry you until your next success helps you recoup your losses. And surely the four months you spent developing the pattern is worth something! Nothing about figuring prices is simple.

(8) KEEP HOME LIFE AND BUSINESS IN PROPORTION. One of the biggest problems with a small home-based business is that you rarely have all the time you need. Because you are home,

people expect more of you than they do of the woman down the street who works at a "regular job". Your husband and your children may not understand that you have certain deadlines that may take precedence over driving for field trips or picking up the dry cleaning.

People tend to think of your business as a hobby, despite financial evidence to the contrary, both in income and in outgo. Your friends may not comprehend the extent of your involvement. In fact, you may have difficulty yourself in remembering that this is now a business. Some women have a hard time deciding what they really want out of it. Do you want a good steady income, or do you just want to putter around? If you're a putterer, your customers will realize it and they will go where they get better service.

(9) USE TIME EFFICIENTLY. The passage of time brings about changes in attitude. Unfortunately, it does not make the day any longer. So find out what you can get done by other people, and pay them to do the busy work. If you hire people on a "contract" basis, you need not pay taxes and social security, but you must file appropriate forms for everyone you pay throughout the year if you intend to deduct the expenses, so keep careful records.

The way I understand it, contract work is work that is done by an individual in *her* choice of location, at *her* speed, using *her* methods. You can set certain guidelines and time limits, of course. At the present time I contract with Nellie, who types my labels, and with Jo, who does my collating and folding, as well as catching up on my filing from time to time. I still get bogged down in paper work, but these women are life-savers.

(10) DEVELOP A SYSTEM OF RECORD-KEEPING EARLY ON. Be flexible about changing it to suit your needs, but start out with *something*, or you will rapidly become bogged down. Here again, my mentor came to the rescue before I had a chance to get into trouble by sending me a copy of a "Daily Balance Sheet" she uses. If you stay on top of that daily record, you can fill in your other records at the end of the month. I always check and double-check my receipts and make sure they balance *before* they go to the bank. Once the checks are out of your hands, it's hard to locate a 42 cents discrepancy.

Because of the nature of your business, you will handle very little cash. As a group, your customers are extremely honest. I have deposited thousands of checks and have had only three that failed to clear. I can see no reason to hold back small orders while waiting for a check to clear. It only frustrates the customer and creates extra work for you. There may be a dollar amount at which you wish to wait for a check to clear, perhaps $20, but that is up to you. Many customers will send money orders to avoid any delays.

(11) **TREAT YOUR CUSTOMERS AS FRIENDS.** You make a lot of friends in mail-order. Despite the numerous letters you receive daily, you begin to recognize names and will exchange notes and get to know each other. Your customer begins to think of you as a friend and she comes to expect certain things from you. If you have led her to expect a quality product and you ship her second-rate goods the next time, she is not likely to forgive you. If you have always shipped promptly and she has to wait for a pattern, she may become annoyed. (Sometimes a trip to the quick-print shop to run off a note of explanation for unavoidable delays is worth the extra couple of dollars.) Your customer may not realize that when you go on vacation, the business goes on vacation too. If you get sick, the business gets sick. Communicate with your customer and let her know she is dealing with a "real person". Without her, you have 1,000 patterns and nowhere to send them.

DAISY ORIGINALS

Anita "Daisy" Winters
PO Box 1136
Denville, NJ 07834-8136
201/625-1446

Established in 1981
Brochure: $.50 (refundable)

18" dresser dolls, six designs crocheted over 2-liter soda bottles.

Anita, the mother of four daughters, paid $75 for her first classified ad - 20 words in a national magazine with a circulation of four million. "A few days after this ad appeared, my post office box was *stuffed* with envelopes," she recalls. "My fortune was made!" Her excitement was short-lived, however, because there was only one order in the fifty envelopes. The rest contained chain letters and get-rich-quick schemes. This pattern continued for the next two weeks, with only five $2 orders and hundreds of pieces of junk mail. Anita felt she had a good product so she did not give up. Instead she tried advertising in a smaller publication directed specifically at crochet lovers. Her $10 ad yielded $40 in orders. "Not a fortune, but definitely encouraging," she says. Today, she has patterns for ponchos, afghans, fridgies and ornaments, as well as her crocheted dolls.

DEBBIE'S DOLLS

Debbie Strickland
Rt. 1, Box 843
Atoka, TN 38004-9801
901/835-3190

Established in 1982
Brochure: $.50

18" nylon-hose Harried Housewife; life-size newborn; handmade dolls; *Dolls to Dollars*, self-published booklet.

Debbie owned 102 dolls when she was 14 years old and still loves them 19 years later. In 1982, laid off by the car dealership she worked for, the mother of three discovered some soft-sculpture dolls at a local craft fair. With some knit fabric and carpet thread, she designed and made her first bald-headed baby. Within a year, she had exhibited at 47 craft fairs, bazaars and flea markets in the Memphis area. Tired of both the physical effort of doing shows and of women buying her dolls and taking them apart to get the pattern, Debbie saved her money and began advertising in a national craft magazine. "Mail-order is a roller coaster ride for sure," she says, "but I love it."

Mail does get lost, says Debbie. "People should write within three or four weeks if they haven't gotten their order. Just write and say 'Where is it?' Most people do, but some, well, are just downright hateful. I had a lady write me three months after I mailed her order. She went on and on about how I was a cheat and how could people 'like me' stay in business. I just wrote her right back that minute. I sent her another pattern, of course, but I didn't say anything ugly. I just told her sometimes mail does get lost. And I told her I never cheated anybody or I wouldn't be in business for long. I did say I was sorry she was so upset, but I couldn't know if the order didn't get there and that I was hoping she would feel better soon as I thought that maybe she was just having a bad day."

DESIGN SOURCE

Nance Kueneman
PO Box 158
Greenleaf, ID 83626-0158
208/454-3100

Established in 1980
Color brochure: LSASE
(double-stamped)

32" to 38" Wall Dolls including Li'l Cowboy, Li'l Cowgirl, Li'l Ballerina, Li'l Football Player, Li'l Basketball Player, Li'l Soccer Player; wool felt (55 colors); trim.

 NANCE'S MARKETING TIPS

Define your market. Do you want to sell directly to the consumer, on consignment to local shops or wholesale to the trade through trade shows? Start at your local library and read, read, read! It's an excellent source of information. Contact the SCORE office at your local Small Business Association; SCORE is a free service made up of retired executives who give advice on any business problems you might encounter. Subscribe to trade magazines in your field.

DESIGN WORKSHOP

Nora Fran Dilks
85 Green Meadow Lane
Telford, PA 18969-2243
215/721-0255

Established in 1980
Catalog: Free with
$.22 postage stamp

20" Daddy's Darling, 20" Little Salt, 15" Suzanne, Alice and Lynette, all with muslin bodies and hand-embroidered faces; 13" Miss Shirley, 16" Wee Willie Winkie, 20" Sandy Sunsuit, 20" Shortenin' Bread, 22" Princess Autumn Moon, 10" Mary and Jerry twins, 8" Victorian Baby Doll, all of polyester knit; 28" Jule-Nissen, Christmas elf from Denmark; 15" Choir Kids; other holiday designs; felt dolls, bears and mice; paper dolls; fabric, including knit velour, polyester knit, muslin; craft felt (9 colors); needles; eyes.

Nora studied fashion design at Moore College of Art in Philadelphia where she received a BFA degree. She went on to design dresses for little girls for the Cinderella Dress Company. "My keen interest in children, knowledge of what they wore and liked, led me to shift my design priorities to children's playthings," says Nora. With the encouragement of a close friend who owned a gift and antique shop, Nora designed a doll. "My daughter was a baby and I was 'housebound' so I made and sold nearly 75 dolls that year," she recalls. Shortly after that, she sold a large lace and net 'Sugar Plum Fairy' to the editors at *McCall's*. "You always remember your first published design!"

Today, Nora works full-time as the director of a Senior Center since she is the sole support of her family. She is also a free-lance designer for *McCall's Needlework and Crafts* and *The American School of Needlework*, teaches craft and doll classes for adult evening school in the spring and fall and runs her own mail-order pattern company.

© DESIGN WORKSHOP

NORA'S MARKETING TIPS

Free-lance designing is a difficult position, especially if you are dependent on a steady income. You get paid *only* for work that is completed *and* published! In addition to being creative, the designer must always be searching for outlets for her work and negotiating publication contracts. Often, after hours of extensive planning and work, a project will not materialize, and, of course, you will not be paid. Many long, hard hours of work can be in vain unless you are mentally able to chalk up your efforts as a learning experience. Learn to assess design proposals, to negotiate and to budget your time and energy into the right channels. Considering the time that goes into most handmade projects, designers of *quality* products never realize their full potential financially.

On the other hand, designing and marketing your own products can be a bit easier than working for someone else. *You* are your own boss and can make the editorial decisions. The trick here is to be able to design a marketable item, package and sell it. Too much diversity usually leads to confusion and drains your own energies. Settle on what you do best and strive to present it to your customers in a concise and attractive manner. When you design a catalog, make it easy to read, eye catching and unique. Never copy another person's individual style and designs because it will not work for you.

All of us who have survived the first years of a small business have found that it is dangerous to borrow money to become established. Move at a pace that suits you and your lifestyle (or should I say nervous system?). Have enough working capital so you will not falter before you get started. The rate of bankruptcies for new businesses ranks somewhere around 90%.

Time is the magic word. If you can learn to manage your creative energies efficiently and still have enough time left for your own personal needs as well as those of your family, you can be a truly successful designer. If your creativity occupies every waking moment to the exclusion of all else, you are robbing yourself of your very essence.

DIMPLE DOLLS BY GEORGIA PO Box 64850 Virginia Beach, VA 23464-0850	21" Bear/Baby; 24" Georgia Baby; 21" Baby Bruin; 18" Huggy Bear; 18" Sleepy Eyes; 21" Tubby Toddler; 16" Cuddly Cub.
DOLLCRAFT PO Box 20104 Albuquerque, NM 87154-0104	16" and 18" Cuddle Kids.

DOLLS BY ANGIE

10013 Manordale Road
Chesterfield, VA 23832-3724

4' Alissa, life-size doll.

DOLLS PATTERNS COSTUMES

Peggy S. Trauger
20 Wendover Road
Rochester, NY 14610-2344
716/482-4662

Established in 1965
Catalog: $1.25

5", 8", 8 1/2", 11", 14", 16" and 18" rag dolls with wardrobes; Pennsylvania doll bonnets (7 styles and 7 sizes).

DOLLS PLUS

Joyce A. Sirard
PO Box 13
Oxford, MA 01540-0013
617/987-5057

Established in 1984
Brochure: $1.25

12" First Baby and clothes, including bunting and crocheted blanket, sunsuits, jeans, shirt and hat, nightgown, pajamas and stocking cap.

In 1981, Joyce wrote to the presidents of two large Boston department stores. "I described my dolls and asked if they would be interested in selling them," she explains. "To my amazement, I heard from both stores." She packed her dolls into a large suitcase and took the subway to Boston on the appointment day. "Both stores loved my dolls and purchased them for that season. I was in heaven. However, I had to have a manufacturer's license and product liability insurance which cost $300 each year." In December 1983, she designed First Baby for her granddaughters Marcelle and Jessica. "I whipped the doll together from a sports sock," she says, "and they loved her." So Joyce began making many First Babies, selling them to area hospital gift shops. Today, she sells the pattern by advertising in national magazines.

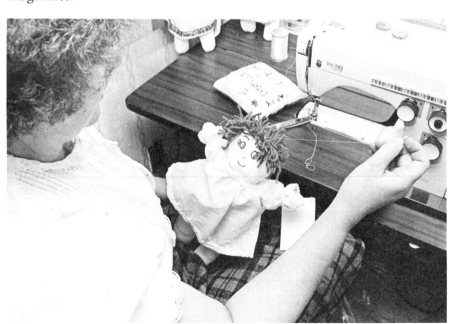

Joyce Sirard, Dollmaker

JOYCE'S MARKETING TIPS

Code your ads so you know exactly where your customers are coming from. Just add a letter to your address - PO Box 13 can become PO Box 13A, PO Box 13B, etc. Keep an accurate mailing list, including the date and item each customer purchased. You will be surprised how many times you refer to the listing.

DOROTHY DEAR OLD FASHIONED DESIGNS

Dorothy B. Smith
PO Box 98
Forest Grove, OR 97116-0098
503/357-7192

Established in 1981
Information: $1

Silk-screened Victorian and country designs; 14"x16" Angel Pillow; 16" Dorothy Dear Doll; 24" Santa Claus; handmade items.

DOTTIE'S DARLINGS

Dorothy C. Nelsen
203 S. Truhn Road
Fowlerville, MI 48836-8931
517/546-5575

Established in 1981
Brochure: $.50

18" to 20" dolls; clothing for 15" to 24" dolls; back packs to hold 18" to 22" dolls; crocheted booties; hats; doll stands; handmade dolls.

Dorothy sells her handmade dolls at craft fairs and doll parties. The hostess booking the party receives a gift of $10, various booking credits and 10% of the gross sales. "The parties have worked out well," says Dorothy. "I just closed my eyes and jumped in." Husband Lee helps out. Their second party had gross sales of $550.

ELF DESIGNS, INC.

Esther Lee Foster
PO Box 76210
Birmingham, AL 35253-6210
205/595-DOLL

Established in 1981
Catalog: Free

Foster Children (15 styles); 11 pattern books; iron-on eyes for 12" to 26" dolls; fabric, fur, wigs; 3 1/2", 5" and 7" needles; plastic doll joints; *The Unicorn*, bimonthly publication.

The doll that Esther designed and made for her granddaughter's fourth birthday was such a success that everyone encouraged her to go into the dollmaking business. "There was no way I could have earned a living at dollmaking," says Esther. "It was much too time-consuming." She knew she could earn much more as a commercial artist/photographer than she could making dolls. After much discussion, Esther decided to combine her skills and write a book with the patterns and directions for her soft-sculpture dolls. "How naive we were!" she says. "I did have lots of graphic arts skills, but I didn't have the foggiest idea of how to market a book and get it out to the public." Once Esther and her businessman husband, Eddie, decided to make the plunge into publishing and promoting, they found that, by combining their skills, they made a pretty good team. "I won't tell you that the first years were easy or that we did everything right," says Esther, "but we learned and we profited from our mistakes. And we have never worked so hard in our lives!"

ELISE PEEPLES DOLLS

3235 SE Taylor
Portland, OR 97214-4270

Brochure: SASE

16" Cozy Anne, recreation of a 19th century pattern.

FANCIFUL DAYDREAMS

PO Box 363
Goshen, IN 46526-0363

Elfie, Jester, Baby Blessing, Toy Soldier, PJ.

FORGET*ME*KNOTS

Dian Specter
103 W. Marshall St.
San Gabriel, CA 91776-4105
818/288-7088

Catalog: $1

16" to 24" jointed pressed felt dolls with clothes; 16" jointed bear; 24" Pinocchio; felt; wigs; wig fur; tights; teeth; plastic joints; criers; eyes (7mm to 10mm); molding mix.

The Lenci company of Turin, Italy began manufacturing felt dolls with seamless faces in the early 1920s. "The machine-pressed faces gave the dolls the lifelike quality of porcelain dolls while preserving the warmth of cloth dolls," says Dian. Today, felt dolls can be made at home, with wool felt dipped into a polymer mix and then hand pressed over a plastic mold. After the face has dried, it is removed, trimmed and sewn into the doll body.

© *Forget*Me*Knots*

GABRIELE'S DOLL STUDIOS

Gabriele Cardy
PO Box F195-91
Blaine, WA 98230
604/531-7996

Established in 1983
Catalog: $2

18" Country Girls (Elizabeth, Diana, Becky) with silkscreened faces and patterns for clothes; 18" Suzy; 13" Cloth China Dolls (Gladis, Lina, Kersten, Gisela) with silkscreened faces and patterns for clothes.

Gabriele has a varied background which includes a freelance art and graphics business which evolved from a custom t-shirt business, as well as publishing a weekly newspaper, several books, signs and graphics. All these experiences taught her silkscreening, marketing, copy-writing and ad layout, but her favorite pastime is drawing and painting faces. With the help and co-operation of her photographer/writer husband and two sons, this desire has become a reality. "The idea and inspiration to create and market cloth doll patterns and silkscreened faces was totally spiritual," says European-born artist Gabriele. "It just came one day like an overwhelming flash."

S·U·Z·Y

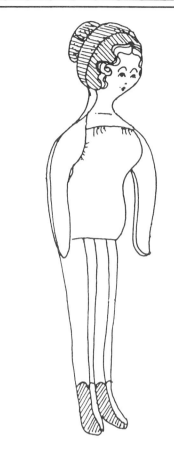

HEAD~ cut 1.

GENE DAWES

3209 Erie Dr.
Orchard Lake, MI 48033-6016

12" clown dolls and Hawaiian dolls.

THE GREEBEE GALLERY

Cyndi Joslyn
11531 St. Paul Ct.
Thornton, CO 80233-2410
303/452-9496

Established in 1981

4" Elvie the Elf, soft-sculptured Christmas ornament.

In 1983, Cyndi decided to mail-order market her best-selling Elvie, a popular Christmas ornament at holiday boutiques. "I thought my product was of primary importance," she says. "If my name was to be on it, I wanted only the finest." So she invested the majority of her capital in the product, including typesetting, a four-color photo on the cover of the pattern and "directions so clear my husband could create an *Elvie*." Cyndi placed a 1/6 page black-and-white ad in a national crafts magazine and received a mediocre response. "If only I knew then what I know now. The most important part of mail-order advertising is THE AD!! I should have spent $2,000 on a beautiful color ad and $400 on the product," she says. "I did it the other way around and now I have no more money to promote a most beautiful product."

Now, she says, the only consolation she has is knowing that the people who took a chance on a small black-and-white ad lost in the multitude of other small black-and-white ads got a quality product and should have hours of fun creating *Elvies*. "Perhaps my experience can help some other would-be designers get their priorities in order to begin with and get off to a successful start," adds Cyndi.

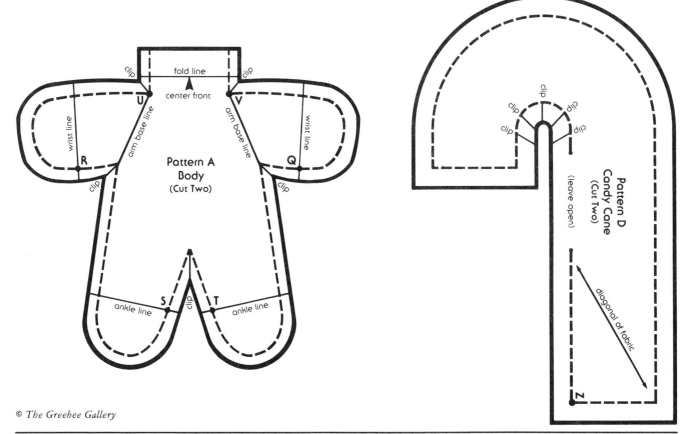

© *The Greebee Gallery*

© Hayseeds

GUILIANI CREATIONS

Nancy Guiliani
PO Box 1239
Ojai, CA 93023-1239
805/646-4563

30" Angelica, hanging doll; 4'8" Patricia; 3'4" Polly; 18" Chubby; handmade dolls.

HANDY HANDS

Jen Kost
Rt. 2, Box 51
Mountainburg, AR 72946-9503
501/369-2585

Established in 1960
List of patterns: $2

Felt and rag dolls; 3 1/2" to 8 1/2" felt mice.

HAYSEEDS

Miriam C. Gourley
1120 E. 300 N.
Pleasant Grove, UT 84062-2547
801/785-8200

Established in 1983
Brochure: Free with LSASE

Cloth dolls, animals and bears, including Kumiko, Ivan and Mildred, Little Women, Oliver Onion Farmer, Bertram and Belinda Bears, Horse of a Different Color, Victoria Rabbit and Her Country Cousin, Thomas and Theodore Teddies; the Santa Fe Collection: Taos Series.

Miriam was an art major at Brigham Young University. She grew up in southern Colorado, near New Mexico, and has always had an appreciation of farm and country art as well as Southwestern art forms.

HEART'S DESIRE

Kristy Clark
PO Box 506
Eureka Springs, AR 72632-0506
501/253-8092

Established in 1979
Color brochure: $1

17" Kristy, 23 1/2" Amanda, 17 1/2" Erin and Adam, 26" Elizabeth, 18 1/2" Robert, 26 1/2" Melissa, 26" Lance, 12 1/2" Emily, all button-jointed dolls.

Kristy Clark, Dollmaker

HEN'S NEST-HOME OF THE "BLOSSOM BABIES"

Faye Wine
PO Box 99
Hiawassee, GA 30546-0099
404/896-3434

Established in 1976
Catalog: $1.50

Blossom Babies, including 22" Morning Glory, 23" Iris, 15" Pansy, 20" Baby Rosebud, 12" Wild Baby's Breath, 22" Angel Trumpet, 15" Blooming Idiot; 22" Black-eyed Susan, etc.; PRO-fessional People, including 20" Tennis Players, Nurse, Doctor, French Waitress, Cook, Cheerleader, Ball Player, Carpenter, Housewife, etc.; handmade dolls; fabrics, including knit, stretch, velour; craft fur; doll wigs.

Faye has been making soft-sculpture dolls since 1974. She also teaches dollmaking and does designs for McCall patterns. Her Blossom Babies aren't always perfect little flowers, she says. *Snapdragon* is a sassy little miss who likes to talk back, *Impatiens* is always in a hurry to do everything and *Forget-Me-Not* is very loving and happy but never remembers anything.

THE HOBBIE HUT

Nola McCarty
PO Box 222
Bedford Park, IL 60499-0222
312/499-3565

Established in 1984
Catalog: $1

18" Kimberly, Melissa, Elizabeth, Peggy, Amanda, Becky and Billy; 20" Betty Jo, Nancy and Grandma; 16" Aussie, koala; handmade dolls.

Nola says her biggest critics are husband Christopher, son Jeff and daughter Kim. "They are tough!!" she admits. "When I get their approval, I know I have a good design." Having a business out of your home takes a great amount of discipline, says Nola. "The distractions are endless. I believe it is easier to have a full-time job away from home."

Nola McCarty, Dollmaker

HOMEY KIDS

Willie Orthmann
Long Pond Road, RFD 3
Dunbarton, NH 03045-9803
603/774-6111

Brochure: $1.50

26" Bobby Baseball, Robbie and Roberta, 21" Sybil (awake and asleep faces), 25" Zachary and Victoria, 20" Brandy, 20" Zeth and Lizzie, all jointed dolls; handmade dolls.

Willie wants her dolls to be cute without being "gooey, sugar sweet". She feels that dolls are messages to the children they are given to and she hopes the message that Homey Kids delivers is that having sex appeal or being super-macho is not what life is all about. "Children need to understand that very few of us are going to look like *Barbie*." says Willie. "It is more important to know who and what we are."

WILLIE'S MARKETING TIPS

Before investing thousands of dollars in a major advertising campaign in national magazines, test the market with ads in smaller, specialized publications. Experiment! Change the ad copy. Perhaps you will draw a better response by using a photograph of group of dolls instead of a single doll. Keep records of the response to each ad and study the results carefully. When you think you have a winner, then you can try the big league!

Willie Orthmann and (from left to right counterclockwise) Victoria, Lizzie, Roberta, Kelly, and Bobby.

I'M STUFFED

Jane Bernardo
PO Box 16853
Tampa, FL 33687-6853
813/985-6590

Established in 1980
Color brochure: $1

9" and 12" Bundle of Joy pillow baby; 15" Cutie Pie and 15" K. C. Jones; 7" to 9" Wibble Wobbles; 9" to 12" cradle angels; 18" Little Homer, 20" Tuff Buck and 21" Ruff Rowdy.

IMAGES BY NAMMY

78 Williams St.
Bradford, PA 16701-1368

Brochure: $1 (refundable)

21" Muffin with outfit.

JEAN'S DOLL PATTERNS

Jean Pickering
1996 Harris
Sheffield Village, OH 44054-2630

Established in 1976
Brochure: $1 and LSASE

21" jointed Red Riding Hood; 22" Cinderella, 22" Prince Charming; 22" Snow White, 12" to 15" Seven Dwarfs, 24" Prince and 23" Queen; 21" Alice; 22" Yankee Doodle; 24" Humpty Dumpty; 20" Mary Had a Little Lamb; 22" Mary Mary Quite Contrary; 20" Miss Muffet and spider; 22" Mermaid; 22" Sleeping Beauty; other dolls.

JUDI'S DOLLS

Judi Ward
PO Box 607
Port Orchard, WA 98366-0607

Color catalog: $1.50

Baby Easy; 22" Gretchen; 22" Bare Baby.

KALICO KASTLE

45 N. Lone Peak Drive
Alpine, UT 84003

Brochure: $1.50

17" New Born Babe; 21" Gingham Dolls.

Mimi's Earth Angel, © Karres Planning Corp.

KARRES PLANNING CORP.

James and Gloria J. "Mimi" Winer
PO Box 662
Point Pleasant, NJ 08742-0662

Established in 1972
Brochure: Free with LSASE

Gloria "Mimi" Winer, Dollmaker

22" jointed Earth Angel fashion doll with seamless face, sculpted trapunto ears and a full wardrobe (lingerie, leotards, blouse, jeans, boots, knitted and crocheted jackets, business suit, purse, attache case, duffle bag and an angelic gown with full wings and removable halo); 14" or 18" Adam and Eve, anatomically-correct newborns with soft spots on the tops of their heads (includes patterns for farm basket bassinet, diaper, nightshirt and bunting); Mimi's Kids, handmade dolls for collectors.

Gloria studied fine art at the National Academy of Art and Design, the School of Visual Arts, the New School/Parsons School of Design and with Pe Ling Liang of New York University. "There is room in the art market-place for all levels of sophistication," she says, "and I would rather have my work in the museum next to Marisol's than on the shelves of games of chance on the Atlantic City Boardwalk." Gloria has a background as an industrial trainer and has worked as a consultant for several Fortune 500 companies. There are three things that Gloria has found necessary for her development as an artist - "the assistance and sharing of information by others, the wherewithal to purchase materials to experiment with to learn my craft and the support of a creative husband who assists me in testing materials, designing tools, photographing my sculpture, writing my public-ity and portfolio, and most of all, who encourages me." Gloria feels that artists need no greater gift than someone to believe in them while they learn to believe in themselves.

KOUNTRY KREATIONS

Evelyn Slayman
19420 Stefani Ave.
Cerritos, CA 90701-7124
213/860-9208

Established in 1984
Brochure: Free

16 1/2" Hollye angel; 3 1/2"x4" Christi, soft-sculptured angel Christmas ornament.

© *Kountry Kreations*

KURLY KUDDLY KIDS

Alice Ann Beecham
1921 Juliet Ave.
St. Paul, MN 55105-1710
612/699-4122

Established in 1982
Catalog: $1.50

14" Jenny with full-color iron-on face transfer and washable stay-in curls; 16" full-jointed Sleepover Suzy; 15" Baby Janet; 22" Baby Beth; 13" Kelly; 18" Dotty Clown; 12" Aunt Maude; 9" Little Phyllis; 7 1/2" Teeny Arline; 9" Alice, Julie and Annie; 9" or 18" Cowboy Billy and Bob; 18" Jo, Ginnelle and Michelle; 14" Mary Jo; wardrobes and accessories; doll stands; fabrics; shoes; fluffy yarn; buttons; trims; lace.

Logo bow-ties led Alice to dollmaking. In the 1960s and 70s, bow-ties were in fashion and husband Bill liked his ties to match his trousers. He would buy the extra long length and Alice would trim off four or five inches and use the fabric to make a custom tie. One day, while shopping in a fabric store, she saw several logo prints and, on a whim, bought several yards of Pepsi Cola fabric. She made some sample ties and shipped them off to the Pepsi company in New York. Pepsi wanted to know just HOW FAST could Alice manufacture the ties? Miller High Life, Schlitz and Pabst were also interested. The Beechams hired local women to sew ties and had a nice little business going until, says Alice, some dumb fashion designer said that anyone who wore a bow-tie looked liked a clown.

"ZAP! There went our business! We were all set up to operate a nice business, but . . . NO BUSINESS." Alice and Bill had learned a lot about buying supplies, packaging, mailing and distribution, but now, the victims of fashion, they needed a product. A chance remark by a granddaughter who asked Santa for a doll that didn't do anything led to a doll design and then another. 14" *Mary Jo* was featured on the July 1979 cover of *Crafts* magazine and things took off from there.

LILLIAN'S COUNTRY CHARM

Mary Lowe
2501 N. Reserve
Muncie, IN 47303-5316
317/282-7526

Established in 1984

Dolls; clowns; witches; 13" calico mouse; other animals.

"When I got married, I hoped for a daughter so I could make pretty clothes and lots of dolls," says Lillian. "I had three sons instead. Now they are all grown, married and have families of their own and I have *lots* of granddaughters."

LINDA'S LADDIES & LASSIES

Linda A. Peters
RR 2, Box 230
Morden, MB
CANADA R0G 1J0
204/822-3305

Established in 1983
Brochure: $1 (refundable with 1st order)

12" to 20" dolls, including Lena, old-fashioned Mennonite girl and 16" Mountie.

LITTLE CHARMERS II

Marilyn Baker Finkey
53430 Hacker Road
Colon, MI 49040-9762
616/432-2344

Established in 1982
Catalog: $1

18" fully-jointed Butch, Eddie and Jo; 16" Biff; 15" Mary Jane; 14" Heather; 25" Chris/Sandra; 24" Molly 17" Ronnie/Renee; 14" Baby Bubbaloo; 13" newborn; 18" Patrick/Peggy; 17" Little Sister; 16" Buffie; 18" Hope; 4' macrame doll swing; fabrics.

LITTLE LOTUS

Loretta Daum Byrne
302 Spring St.
Cambridge, WI 53523-9219

Established in 1977
Brochure: $1 and LSASE

22" basic doll pattern with set-in eyes, clothing and Afro, Anglo and Asian doll faces; 22" Gilly Moko (outer space child); 20" Red Feather and Little Turtle (Woodland Indian mother and baby); Ping Panda; Toby Chimp; 5" and 8" folk figures; 2" to 8" Wee Folk, including dollhouse family and pets, faeries and winged creatures, elves, gnomes, trolls, unicorn, dragon, etc.; 4 1/2" to 8" Christmas Wee Folk, including Mr. and Mrs. Santa, tree, elves, reindeer, snowsuit children, sleigh, sled; Circus Wee Folk, including performers, clowns, bear, dog, lion, tiger, camel, elephant, horse; old-fashioned dolls' clothes; *Anne Marie*, a 16-page pattern booklet for a 17" Turn of the Century Doll; other designs for dolls, animals and costumes.

Loretta's dolls were originally designed for families like hers who had adopted children of various ethnic or racial groups that did not match their own. "I felt that having a doll that looked like the child who owned it would help that child develop a better self-image," she says. At that time, in 1975, she could not find any dolls made of stretch knit fabric with fingers and toes, set-in eyes and fur fabric hair.

Loretta has a deep personal interest in people of the world, their clothing and customs, as well as an avid interest in animals. A regular columnist for *Needle & Thread*, *Needlecraft for Today* and *The Needle People News*, her designs are frequently seen in *Country Handcrafts*, *Crafts*, *Needle & Thread* and *Needlecraft for Today*. "One of my greatest delights is that my husband and I design many projects jointly for *Country Handcrafts* magazine," she says. She has shown her watercolors and fabric wallhangings at several invitational shows and one-woman shows and was the designer/creator of 23 carpet murals for an insurance company in Ft. Worth. At present, Loretta is working on five life-size soft-sculpture figures for the Wisconsin State Historical Society's museum in Madison.

Loretta Daum Byrne, Dollmaker

 LORETTA'S MARKETING TIPS

I like selling through mail-order and a few choice galleries. I look for galleries that have a cheerful atmosphere from the moment you walk into them simply because I have always wanted my artwork to make people feel good. In my mail-order business, I insist on answering each letter personally. This sometimes holds up an order, but I feel that a personal answer is appreciated.

From the Little Lotus Collection.
© *Little Lotus*

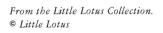

LITTLE OLD LADY ORIGINALS

Elinor Peace Bailey
1779 East Ave.
Hayward, CA 94541-5401
415/582-2702

Established in 1982
Brochure: $.50

28" Victorian Doll; 28" Pierrot and Pierrette; 9" Mini Pierrot and Victorian Doll; Bean Bottom Dolls and Four Poster Bed; Tumbling Angel; Baroque Angel; St. Nick; Plain Old Rag Doll; Bo-Peep and Boy Blue; Shady Lady and Dapper Dan; Mother Cat and Kittens.

Elinor graduated as an art major from Brigham Young University and has done further studies at Tyler School of Fine Arts, Parsons School of Design and San Jose State. The mother of nine is a designer, teacher, lecturer and writer. More than 7,000 patterns for her Victorian doll have been sold in the past three years. "If you love fabric, you'll love my dolls," she says.

Elinor Peace Bailey, Dollmaker

© *Little Old Lady Originals*

LITTLE PUNKIN PATTERNS

Julie Jensen
PO Box 1380
Woodbridge, CA 95258-1380
209/369-7269

Established in 1984
Brochure: $1

*Julie Jensen, Dollmaker and
Little Punkin*

19" Jenny, Lisa and April; 20" Kelly; 13" Country Sweethearts (3 styles).

 JULIE'S MARKETING TIPS

Consider unusual markets for your handmade dolls. Interior decorators and decorating accent shops are a wide open, relatively untapped market. Decorators and their clients are very interested in folk art-type country dolls and other dolls and toys suitable for decorating. Open any country decorating magazine and you'll see dolls, calico bears or toys in nearly every room setting. Workmanship must be of the highest caliber and originality is important. Offer to do special orders to co-ordinate with any interior. Also, consider exclusive children's boutiques. Some want dolls and toys as part of an exclusive gift line. Many simple life-size dolls can be marketed and sold as mannequins to these shops.

LITTLE RIVER CRAFTS

PO Box 1086
Ft. Payne, AL 35967-1086

5" to 6" Numpkins.

LOVE ME DOLLS

Wanda Morris
PO Box 1060
Logansport, LA 71049-1060
318/697-4849

Established in 1977
Brochure: $1 and SASE

Betty Boop; 21" Jason Cowboy and Joy Cowgirl; 18" Dee Dee; 21" Donny, Joe and Jenny; 21: Mistress Mary; 21" Red Riding Hood; 24" Mother Goose; 18" Wee Willie Winkie; 21" Miss Muffet; 21" Pinocchio; 21" Ballerina; 21" Cheerleader; 21" Football Star.

THE MAIL POUCH

Marilyn Ellis
PO Box 1373
Monrovia, CA 91016-1373
818/579-9088

Established in 1977
Color catalog: $3

Victorian Pillow Doll; Victorian Christmas Doll; Jeremy and Jenny; Little Lisa; Folk Art Santas; Mr. and Mrs. Santa Dolls and Country Couple; Tree Top and Baby Angel.

MARIE LOUISE ORIGINALS

15802 Springdale St.
Huntington Beach, CA 92649-1728

Catalog: $1.50

25" Katrina and 25" Huck, doll kits.

MATERIAL MEMORIES

Pamela Harrison Weaver
PO Box 39
Springville, NY 14141-0039
716/496-7555

Established in 1983

13" Dixie; 15" Amish Girl and Goose; 16" Amish Boy; 16" Topsy Turvy; 20" Country Chicken; Good Luck Duck; Folk Art Cat.

Pamela started her business with exactly $1567. "The first mistake I *almost* made," she admits, "was to hire a lawyer to help me with copyrighting. His fee was going to be $500, but I found out I could do it myself for $20." She wrote letters to craft magazines asking about ad rates. Initial printing expenses were $329 and her first ad cost $875. Other expenses such as artist's drawings and a post office box number brought Pamela very close to her budget. "I can remember going to my PO Box the first time and was I happy!" she says. Soon small shop owners were ordering her patterns for retail sales. "My small business is growing very fast," says Pamela. "I have never been to college and have taken no business courses. If I can do it, anyone can!"

© *Material Memories.*

MISS MARTHA ORIGINALS

Martha Holcombe
PO Box 5038
Glencoe, AL 35905-0038

Catalog: $1 and SASE

20" Preshus; 22" Mr. T; 17" Baby Sonshine; iron-on-face transfer for 16" to 18" dolls and for 22" adult ethnic dolls; iron-on-eyes.

© *Miss Perky's Patterns*

MISS PERKY'S PATTERNS

Dorothy Everds
215 Summit Dr., Tower Lakes
Barrington, IL 60010-1149
312/526-7829

Established in 1982
Brochure: $.50

Dorothy Everds, Dollmaker

16" Waldo Clown; Keystone Kop and Harlequin costumes for Waldo; 12" Betsy Ross; 15" and 14" Farmer in the Dell and his Wife; 15" Sister Sue and Brother Billy Bob; 11" Crab and 14" Lobster.

Dorothy started making dolls during the Great Blizzard of '79 in Illinois.* Her husband John, who illustrates children's books, made sketches which he thought would make cute characters. "I kept sewing while it kept snowing and by the spring thaw, I had completed about fifteen little creatures," she recalls. They were able to sell these designs to *Better Homes & Gardens* for publication in one of their craft/needlework magazines. After several of these sales during the next two years, Dorothy decided to answer the challenge of publishing her own patterns. She became fast friends with a printer and a typesetter and learned the realities of buying advertising space and planning ahead. "My business is small and personal," she says. "I enjoy the occasional letters from customers, many of whom are grandmothers who live in the country or in small towns and who sew for their grandchildren. I am still unsure about the need to grow bigger, risking the danger of becoming a catalog producer instead of a designer."

*I remember it, Dorothy. That's *exactly* when I started researching and writing my first guidebook to Chicago-area art and craft shows, which led to *Crafts Woman* magazine, which led to *this* book. Look at all the things that can get done when you're snowed in three months each year!

Miss Perky's Patterns
© 1982

FARMER IN THE DELL
and HIS WIFE

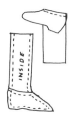

Farmer's Shoes: Sew leg sections to shoe tops. Right sides together, sew back seams, leaving open at top and bottom.

Make tiny cuts at center ends of each sole. Match cuts to front and back leg seams. Baste sole to shoe top. Machine stitch very close to edge all around. Turn and stuff, leaving 1" at top of leg unstuffed. Stitch shut.

Farmer's Wife: Shoe has no sole. Sew leg sections to shoe tops. Reverse position so that there will be a right and left side. Place together and stitch along back leg, around bottom edge of shoe and up the front leg. Leave open at the top. Turn and stuff, leaving 1" at top unstuffed. Stitch shut.

Sew legs across bottom front edge of torso. SHOES SHOULD POINT IN TOWARD TORSO AS YOU STITCH.

Clear directions make Miss Perky's patterns easy to use.

MATERIALS FOR CLOTHING

¼ yd. or remnants of the following:

Red gingham for farmer's shirt and wife's apron.
Calico print for wife's dress
Dark blue cotton for farmer's overalls.
4 small white buttons   6 small snaps

1 9" x 12" piece of tan felt for hats or purchase straw hats in craft dept.

GENERAL INSTRUCTIONS:

Use a small machine stitch. Reinforce stitching at start and finish of seams by backstitching. Use a screwdriver as a stuffing tool. Use ample amounts of fiberfill for a firm and shapely doll. Instead of cutting the pattern pieces apart, use carbon paper and transfer patterns on the back of fine sandpaper. Cut out each piece and label. Lay on felt and trace around edge with a sharp pencil. The sandpaper adheres to the felt and assures an accurate cut. The patterns can be used many times. Take the time to baste.

DIRECTIONS FOR BODY (Cont.)

Match centers and baste seat section through front torso and leg thicknesses. Stitch firmly by hand or machine, leaving back open for stuffing.

Stuffing: Starting with a small amount in the nose, gradually add more fiberfill 'till head is firmly shaped. Finish stuffing the torso. Close the back seat with overcast handstitching.

Arms: Right sides together, stitch arm pieces, leaving open at top. Turn and stuff. Slipstitch closed around tab.

Define fingers with four rows of handstitching. Using a double thread, insert needle in side seam and bring up where finger starts. Quilt in and out, pulling thread tight. Finish with a hidden knot.

Attach arm as shown in diagram with firm overcast stitches.

Eyes: Cut two white eyes according to diagram. Using thin glue, place eyes where marked. Insert needle threaded with black floss in back of head (knot will be covered with hair later.)

Bring out at center of eye and embroider an iris.

ACTUAL SIZE

MY TY CREATIONS

806 Main St.
Hays, KS 67601-4441

Color brochure: $1 and SASE

21" bride with 29" train and bridesmaid; 20" Tara with three outfits; 8" Quiet Dolls in case; 16" Ginny in back-pack.

NORTH COUNTRY DOLLS

Susan C. Shell
PO Box 175
Caroga Lake, NY 12032-0175
518/835-6060

Established in 1979
Brochure: $1

15 1/2" Peggy, Mandy, Carmi, Gladys; 15" Emma, Bonnie, Janet, Delores and Cousin Delia; 19" Emily; 12" baby doll; 14" Joan and 18" Jane; 14" Brownie; 13 1/2" Lisa; 13" Sleepy Baby; 11 1/2"Topsy and Eva (two-headed doll); 12" Patches; 12 1/2" dolls (6 styles); 10" Easter Rabbit.

Susan's patterns are adaptations of old ones. Despite three major professional career changes (from a cooperative extension home economist to a physical education teacher to a registered nurse), her interest in dolls remains constant and she is planning to expand her pattern selection soon.

© North Country Dolls.

OSAGE COUNTY QUILT FACTORY

Virginia Robertson
400 Walnut, PO Box 490
Overbrook, KS 66524-0490
913/665-7500

Established in 1978
Color catalog: $1

Velma and Thelma doll; 12" Marie-Claude; 22" Rita Doll; Lucy Pillow Doll; Jinny Jo Doll; Ima T. Cozy; Cinderella; Dina Doll; Lucy Goose; Angie Angel ornament; also doll patterns by Elinor Peace Bailey (see LITTLE OLD LADY ORIGINALS) and others; needles; quilter's pins; fabric spray adhesives.

When Virginia was working on her Master's in fine arts at Idaho State University, she began to notice that all her paintings looked like quilts. Since fabric paintings were not permitted as part of her degree work, she waited until graduation to explore the medium further. In the late 1970s, she began to make cloth dolls for a quilt shop and, thanks to a New York City agent, got more orders than she could handle. Macy's, Spiegel, Saks Fifth Avenue, as well as gift shops all over the country, ordered her dolls faster than she and her ten helpers could make them. The largest order came from Spiegel - for 500 triangle dolls. The inevitable outcome was "burn-out".

There was little time to design and be creative and Virginia decided she didn't really want to be famous. She began to publish the pattern for one of the dolls she designed and the retail business was phased out over the next two years and replaced with a wholesale pattern business. Today, Virginia and her husband Lynn have converted a turn-of-the-century Methodist church into a quilt supply shop where they stock 1,500 bolts of fabric, 2,000 books and patterns, quilting supplies and gift items. Classes in quilting and dollmaking are held in the basement. Virginia's doll and quilt patterns are sold to 1,200 stores nationwide and eight distributors.

© Osage County Quilt Factory

THE PATTERN PLACE

Connie Ellsworth
856 E. 275 South
Payson, UT 84651-2320
801/465-4642

Established in 1979
Catalog: $1

12", 16" and 24" Tiny Tots; 16" Mandi and 17" Matt; 20" Steffany and Tiffany; 14" Baby Emily; 26" Tami; 27" Ross and Jeff; 10" Heather and Hanna, upside-down doll; 16" Big Sister Josie; 23" Toby and Tish; 22" Clown-ee and 15" Clarence, clowns.

The Ellsworths started their pattern business on $30. They were broke at the time, so they placed flyers in stores and on bulletin boards. "It has not been easy," says Connie. "It's been a lot of hard work! We now have seven children and, believe me, it is a BIG challenge juggling priorities." They recently negotiated a contract with a toy manufacturing company for two of Connie's designs.

Tiffany and Steffany,
© *The Pattern Place*

PATTERN PLUS

Rainie Crawford
21 Mountain View Ave.
New Milford, CT 06776-4725

Catalog: $1.50

Pookie babe, Rocky hobby horse and Poco bear; 19" Mary-Ellen, a topsy-turvy doll in christening gown; 15" Sugar 'n Spice, a topsy-turvy bear doll; 11" Joy; 16" Annabelle; 9 1/2" and 11 1/2" Bagel, bears.

PATTERNS BY JOAN

PO Box 6103
Greenwood, IN 46142-6103

21" Bonnie Bloomers and 23" Ronnie Rompers.

PETRONELLA PATTERNS

Mary Pat Warren
1672 Donelwal Dr.
Lexington, KY 40511-9021
606/233-7922

Established in 1979
Color brochure: Free with LSASE

15" to 25" sock dolls, including 25" Sad Sack Clown, 21" Hobo Clown, 18" Heart Clown, 22" Circus Clown, 22" Woeful Will, 22" Dandy Andy; 21" Scarecrow, 24" Witch, 21" Santa and 20" Mrs. Claus and 10" Elves; 15" Angel, 24" Rabbit.

© Petronella Patterns

PIECES OF OLDE

Nancy Wertheimer
5614 Greenspring Ave.
Baltimore, MD 21209-4308
301/466-4949

Established in 1980
Brochure: $1

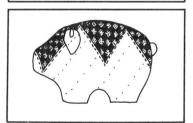

14" Little Folk and 3 1/2" Patches; Liza and Kate, topsy-turvy doll; Plain People; 21" Hugging Bear; 20" Country Hare; 18" Olde Time Piggy; 8" to 12" Folkart Animals, including cat, duck, rabbit, pig, bear; handmade dolls and animals.

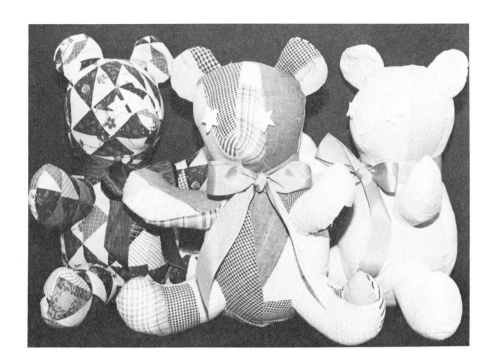

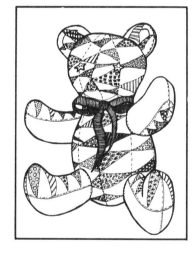

© *Pieces of Olde*

THE PIG WORKS

Margaret L. Butler
PO Box 1305
Woodland Hills, CA 91365-1305

Established in 1980
Brochure: $1

16" Mr. Pillow Doll and Mrs. Pillow Doll; 7" Winnie Witch and Mr. Pumpkin; 12" Poppy the Unicorn/Rocking Horse.

From the Platypus Collection.
© *Platypus*

PLATYPUS

Colette Wolff
Box 396, Planetarium Station
New York, NY 10024-0396
212/874-0753

Established in 1970
Catalog: $1

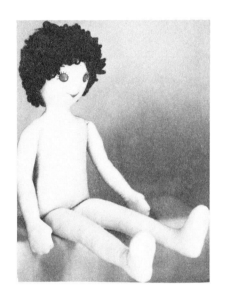

19" Bridgit; 24" Veronica (1760, 1775, 1790, 1805, 1860, 1885 costumes); 19" Penelope (with six costumes - 1830, Puritan, Little Red Riding Hood, Princess, Norwegian, Contemporary); 13" Sally and Sebastian; 8" Debbie; 5" Abigail; 14 1/2" Funny People (9 personalities); 20" Minerva the Mermaid, 26" Dragon and 13" Unicorn; 25" Sir Gore the Dreaded Black Knight; 24" Giggle the Anxious Jester; 18" Phoebe the Contemporary Peddler Doll; 7 1/2" Muslin Angel; 17" Platypus; 13 1/2" Armadillo and 4 1/2" Bird; 7" Starfish and 7 1/2" Crab; Menagerie of Little Stuffed Animals, including owl, lion, elephant, rabbit, pig, hippopotamus and penguin; African Silhouette Animals, 13 designs; 10" Hen and 4" Chicks; 11" Cat and 3 1/2" Mouse; 61" seven-car Fantasy Train and 3 1/2" Trainmen; *Teaching a Sock Doll Workshop*; *The Fine Art of Stuffing Cloth Dolls and Animals*; *The Fine Art of Making Faces on Cloth Dolls*, three self-published booklets; 100% cotton muslin; buttons; needles; lace and eyelet; craft fur.

Colette began with a $9 classified ad in a little craft magazine. The ad was a success so she designed more dolls, placed more ads and read every book about mail-order she could find. "Then I got together a small catalog," she recalls. "I organized record keeping systems, designed forms for everything and graduated from a mimeograph machine to offset reproduction." For ten years the business was an extra activity, with new patterns appearing sporadically. By 1979 Colette decided that her pattern business had to progress or be phased out.

Deciding that it had developed enough of a reputation and catalog to become the basis for a full-time profit-making business, Colette began placing display ads in mass circulation craft and needlework magazines. Soon the business was devouring 60 to 70 hours of her time each week. Help was hired, the logo was re-designed, photographs were added to the catalog, wholesale business was encouraged and the first bulk mailing was sent out. Everything was done manually, including an 18,000 piece bulk mailing. "It was madness!" she admits. Their mailing list was computerized in 1983 and mailings are now done by a lettershop.

THE RAG DOLL

Marge Crunkleton
PO Box 456
Denver, NC 28037-0456

Brochure: $1

3" to 10" sock dolls; Kimmie Poo; infant-size dolls; 6" to 12" Sweet Babies, sock dolls.

RAGGEDY JOAN'S DOLLS

Joan A. Cosner
10436 Midway St.
Bellflower, CA 90706-5048
213/925-5300

Established in 1980
Brochure: $1

13" Connie Conestoga; 17" Millie the old English Notion Nanny; 18" Sweetie and Friend; 17" Wendy; 13" Kewtie Babies; 11" Chef Basil; 25" Dressed Chick; 11" Crackers and Cheese, mouse couple.

RAINBOW WORLD

Barbara Carroll
PO Box 608
Lebanon, OR 97355-0608
503/258-2243

Established in 1979
Brochure: $1.25

57 doll and animal patterns including 16" Rivet and 14" Hot Lips the Frog Couple.

Rivet and Hot Lips. © Rainbow World.

RAYNA

Mildred Elkin
PO Box 37
Dunedin, FL 34296-0037
813/796-1225

Established in 1983
Brochure: Free

20" Baby Rayna and Little Rayna; 36" Rayna; craft fur (6 colors); doll joints; floss; needles.

"Necessity," says Mildred, "forced me to sew and design my own clothes in high school. Most of them were made from garments previously worn by relatives." She started college at age 16, planning to become a doctor, but soon realized that she had to become self-supporting as soon as possible. "So I became a high school science teacher until my daughter, Rayna, was born." Today, the Elkins own a retail store, *Craft Harbor* in Clearwater, Florida, where Mildred teaches crafts and now Rayna is planning to be a doctor.

SAN LOU

Sandra Price
PO Box 70876
Marietta, GA 30007-0876
404/992-7186

Established in 1981
Brochure: $.50

22" and 26" "Real Children" and "Real Baby".

SEW LOVABLES

1003 E. 3rd St.
Dover, OH 44622-1223

Catalog: $.50

10" to 18" dolls with seamless faces; puppets.

SEW SPECIAL

Judiann Irons
2762 Londonderry Dr.
Sacramento, CA 95827-1317
916/362-5118

Established in 1982
Catalog with color photos:
$1.50

18" Just Plain Kids; 16" Holly and Peppermint; 23" Cookie Crumblers; 15" anatomically-correct Baby Beth and Baby Bret; 5" Little Pocket Friend; 19" Gypsy Love; 16" Judiann's Angel; 16" Tea Time Cousins; 16" Sheriff and Little Nel; 16" Graduate; 14" John and Priscilla; 10" Choir Boys; 9" Christmas Angels; 14" Bride and Groom; 18" Lucky Leprechaun and Erin; 24" 24-Carrot Bunny; 10" and 20" Witches; 25" Santa and Mrs. Santa and their elves 10" Mighty Sweet, 18" McHappy and 18" Doc; Christmas ornaments, including 5" Guardian Angel, 3 1/2" Bearly an Angel, 3 1/2" Tiny Ted, Rocky (pony, reindeer, unicorn, Pegasus); 16" Drummer Boy; 16" Sugar Plum Fairy; fabrics, including velour, knit; buttons.

"I had always dreamed I would have little girls to make dolls for," says Judiann, "but I had two sons so, as an outlet for my frustration, I began making dolls for other people."

 JUDIANN'S MARKETING TIPS

If you want a mail-order business, do your homework. Read everything you can get your hands on regarding mail-order marketing. Go slow, be careful and let experience be your best teacher.

Doc, Mighty Sweet, and McHappy Christmas elves. © Sew Special

SEW-SO-EASY

Bonnie MacRae
PO Box 736
Churchville, VA 24421-0736

Catalog and sample newsletter: $1 (refundable with order)

© Sew-So-Easy

24 1/2" Michelle, 32" Duo the Clown; 19" Little Princess; 19" La Prima Ballerina; 23" Rapunzel; 18 1/2" Becky and 18 1/2" Tom Sawyer; 11" Baby Wee Bairn; 20" Goldilocks; 10 1/2" Little Doctor; 9" Tree Top Angel; 15" or 30" Wonderful Alice; 8 1/2" Unicorn; 32 other designs; ponte knit (caramel, baby face, peaches and cream, vanilla, cocoa); cotton broadcloth (pale peach); craft fur.

Bonnie studied at the Fashion Institute of Technology in New York City and worked as a fashion illustrator where she became accustomed to the pressure and pace of corporate advertising campaigns and nationally-distributed catalog illustration assignments. But she began her career in the art department of her hometown newspaper in Augusta, Georgia. "It was wonderful training in process and technique," she says. "When you work in a small newspaper, you get involved in every aspect of printing as you supervise the reproduction of your art work. Thanks to such hands-on printing experience, I can oversee all steps of pattern production."

SHARI DOLLS

PO Box 1863
Beaufort, SC 29901-1863

Information: $.35

17" Julie in lace-trimmed dress and booties.

SPRINGTIME

Marilyn Jensen
4860 Ontario Way
Santa Maria, CA 93455-5704

12" jointed baby Dawn.

STITCH 'N STUFF

Dolores Smith
4900 Winthrop West
Ft. Worth, TX 76116-8287
817/738-0545

Established in 1976
Information: $1

13"x20" Rowdy Rooster Weathervane; 24" Buffy Ballerina; 14" Dr. Phil 'n Good; 16" Noah Pocket Doll; 15" Penny Angel; 17" Cinderella Upside-Down Doll.

STORYBOOK EDITIONS

PO Box 426
Van Wert, OH 45891-0426

Silkscreened muslin doll kits with handpainted faces.

SUGAR PLUM CREATIONS

Marsha Webster
PO Box 2914
Hesperia, CA 92345-1111
619/244-9741

Established in 1983
Brochure: $.50

16" Tracy and Pup; 11" Hattie; 14" Baby Tara; 18" Sugar Babe; 14" Christin and Bunny; 26" Tricia; 15" Santa Claus and Mrs. Claus; 15" Leprechaun; 16" Miss Peggy Piggy; 18" Clown; 17" Sugar Bear; 20" Bernard Bear; 6" Mousie; other designs.

© Sugar Plum Creations.

T.E.M. OF CALIFORNIA

Tressa E. Mabry
PO Box 4311
Fullerton, CA 92634-4311
714/871-8210

Established in 1975
Color brochure: $.50

12" Jenny, Baby Sue, Annie, Todd, Chad; 17" Old-Fashioned Lady; 11 1/2" Nettie Fashion Doll and 9 costume sets (1840 Christmas; 19th century bridal, Easter, 1870 parlor, 1830 spring medley; 1880 carriage, 1890 gay nineties, 1910-1920 trolley, 1800 empire).

TECHE COUNTRY

Caroline C. Verret
408 Birch St.
New Iberia, LA 70560-1906
318/369-7467

Established in 1984
Information: SASE

16" Evangeline, Queen of the Teche; 16" Jean Lafitte; 13" Popee and Popette, mice; 19" Molly; 18" Pockets, dog; 21" Fun Frog, with lily pad.

Two of Caroline's dolls are based on local Louisiana personalities - Longfellow's Evangeline and Jean Lafitte, the pirate who was enlisted by General Andrew Jackson to help defend New Orleans against the British during the Battle of New Orleans. "These two people have been favorites of mine since childhood," she says.

TERIAN

Janet S. Thigpen
PO Box 318
Albuquerque, NM 87103-0318
505/256-7794

Established in 1978
Information: SASE

Bottle Baby; 8" Petite Doll; 15" Pioneer Doll; 48" Big Doll; 12" Penny Doll; 30" Boudoir Doll.

Janet's six dolls were originally made for her daughter, Teri Annette. The Bottle Baby, e.g., was designed with arms and legs in a permanently bent position to hold Teri's bottle while Janet fed and bathed her older brothers. That was in 1960. Today, Teri is grown with a family of her own and Janet works full-time for the city of Albuquerque. Janet says she made "several very bad mistakes" when she first started her business in 1978: (1) underestimating the cost of advertising, (2) overestimating the returns from advertising, (3) underestimating the amount of time it would take to run the business, (4) not creating or even knowing HOW to create a sound business plan and (5) not allowing for LIFE.

THREEFOLD CORD CREATIONS

Wanda Ragsdale
PO Box 7463
Tyler, TX 75711-7463
214/561-9597

Established in 1983

Chosen Children, including 15" Rainbow, Candace and Michele; 19" Stacie, Tracy, Regan, Megan, Nicole, Kristiana, Hannah and Vanessa.

TWYLA-DOLLS

2618 N. 9th St.
West Monroe, LA 71291-5140

19" Claire with her own doll, Ginger.

WAVERLY LYNN

Judy Showalter
PO Box 762
Coupeville, WA 98239-0762

Button Nose Kids, including 18" Aimee Rae with baby swing; 20" Kelley; 18" Gretchen; 18" anatomically-correct Todd; 8 other doll designs; 30" Papa Bear, 27" Mama Bear and 18" Baby Bear; 4 puppets.

Judy, the mother of three, spent twelve years designing stuffed toys and baby articles for national manufacturing companies. Disillusioned with her job, she decided to start her own design business in 1981. Husband Lars was supportive and now the entire family is involved. Judy's patterns are now being produced and distributed by Sylvia Folkart of Folkart Publishing (PO Box 1105, Coupeville, WA 98209-1105).

Judy Showalter, Dollmaker

WEE WONDER WORKS

PO Box 552
Russell, IA 50238-0552

18" 3-in-1 Storybook doll (Red Riding Hood, Grandma and Big Bad Wolf).

THE WELCH GANG

Marcella Welch
5475 Rt. 193
Andover, OH 44003-9735
216/293-7380

Established in 1979
Brochure: $.25

Slumbering Babes; life-size Mama; Marcy; 14" Personality Purse; four-way stretch nylon; needles; mohair roving; wool roving.

Marcella is a black dollmaker who tries to design black dolls with a message. "Some of my dolls have been criticized as being stereotypical of blacks although I use people I know as models." Her work was censored once at a gallery show. "Some of the black women objected to my large black woman doll," she says. "It was later removed from the show. The director said censorship of this type was unheard of."

 MARCELLA'S MARKETING TIPS

Have more than one pattern when you are starting out. Most money is made from satisfied customers who re-order patterns and supplies. Some people frown on the practice of advertising two items in the same ad, but I have found it helpful if the items are related, such as *Mama* with a *Slumbering Babe* in her arms.

Marcella Welch, Dollmaker, and The Welch Gang

ALICE & LEE WELPLEY

6585 Pleasant Valley Road
Diamond Springs, CA 95619-9601
916/626-3498

Established in 1974
Information: Free

Pressed felt dolls, including 23" Alice, 17" Butterfly, 17" Victor or Vicky, 31" Barbara, 16" Connie, 17" Chloe; *How to Make a Pressed Felt Doll*, self-published booklet; wool felt; head and limb disc sets; hydrastone matrix molds.

Alice Welpley, Dollmaker

WIL-MAR CREATIONS

PO Box 3422
Kissimmee, FL 32742-3422

14 1/2" Angela.

WILLOWOOD

PO Box 31301
Cincinnati, OH 45231-0301

Established in 1983
Information: $.50

22" Katy and 9" Puppy; 20" Noel and 6" Fawn; 22" Bo Peep and 9" Lamb; 20" Kelly and 6" Kitty.

WOOGAMS ORIGINALS

Addie Lynn Smith
PO Box 68
Centerville, UT 84014-0068
801/292-4972

Established in 1982
Color brochure: $1

8" Diaper Bag Baby, 18" Addie Lynn or Lacci Bride Doll, Niki, Jenny, Angie; 12" or 18" Grandma Hattie, Willa Kitchen Witch, Karleen; 2", 3", 4", 9" 14" wig frames for wigmaking; 7" to 10" mouse family.

Kelly and Kitty
Bo Peep and Lamb
© *Willowood*

YOUNG LUVS

Linda Young
8423 Eton Ave.
Canoga Park, CA 91304-2733
818/998-1580

Established in 1983
Brochure: Free

28" silk-screened Medical Doll; 15" ME Doll.

Linda and her husband, the parents of four young children, the original Young Luvs, designed a basic anatomy doll to teach children about their bodies. The Medical Dolls have been placed in numerous hospitals, schools and homes. "The doll," says Linda, "is our dedication to a very close friend, John Hauser, a kidney-dialysis patient for eighteen years, who received his third kidney transplant early in 1985."

© Young Luvs

BONNIE LYNN YOUNG

314 S. Clinton Ave.
Lindenhurst, NY 11757-5123
516/226-7885

Established in 1984
Brochure: $1

12 1/2" Amish Doll with tiny quilt; Folk Art Doll.

 BONNIE'S MARKETING TIPS

When selling patterns through mail-order, the publication you choose is most important. Spend the money for a display ad because it will pay for itself if you are in the right publication. Sometimes I have been so bold as to walk into quilt shops to show my samples and patterns, dressed in my patchwork clothing with a basket on my arm. The samples certainly sell the patterns! The shop owners are very curious to see what I have in the basket!

CHAPTER
2

Soft Animal & Bear Patterns & Kits

The most variety and creativity is found in the cloth animal and bear patterns and kits. Since so many creatures are collectible, many of the 84 designers in this chapter have directed their energies towards keeping a well-populated zoo. Aardvarks to zebras and everything in between has been captured in cloth. There is a pattern for a 9' boa, a Pteranodon with a 50" wing span, a 34" manatee and a 26" mola bird. Creativity doesn't seem to stop when it comes to picking names for some of these cloth creatures: Plaid Thad the Armadillo, Friliphants and Plato Pegasus can be found within this section.

AARDVARK TO ZEBRA

Lois Boncer
219 El Arbol Dr.
Carlsbad, CA 92008-4317
619/438-3431

Established in 1972
Catalog: $1

21" aardvark; 13" pig; 10" duck; 11" and 17" bison; 9" and 18" dodo; 10" and 13" koala; 25" anteater; 14" sloth; 13" unicorn; 12" hobby horse/unicorn; 4" and 20" sow with piglets; 13" rabbit; 29" dragon; 16" and 18" parrot, cockatoo and toucan; 14" zebra; 16" moose; 15" and 20" bears; 26" sea otter; other animal and doll designs; handmade animals and dolls; *Aardvark to Zebra*, a 259-page 9"x12" pattern book.

Lois designs and sells more than 250 kinds of animals, dolls and mythological beasts from many cultures. Only ten percent of these designs are available in pattern or kit form at this time. Her full-length pattern book, recently published by New Century Publishers, contains many of her designs; two new books are in the works. Lois teaches courses on creative dollmaking at her local community college and serves as president of a co-operative of artists and craftspeople and as program chairwoman of another. "I'm doing my best to educate the public as to the value of handcrafted items," she says.

   LOIS'S MARKETING TIPS

At craft fairs, smile and speak to everyone going by. Invite them into your booth. You can do this without seeming "pushy". I sit at a table near the front of my work and *work*. I have the machine work done on a basketful of animals and dolls, so I can sit and stuff them and do the handwork. People come close to see what I am doing. I show those who are interested how to do whatever I'm doing (and often sign up students for my classes). While my hands are busy, my mouth is free to smile and talk. I can lay the work down at any time to pick up a handmade animal for a customer or to write up an order. Also, because I'm *doing* something, I am often chosen by the photographers or camera crew (and that's free publicity!). Business cards help a lot. I sell hundreds of items at Christmas time to people who picked up my card at a craft fair in April or August.

I've done some display advertising in magazines, but have never gotten enough orders to pay for the ads. I have had magazines print one of my patterns with instructions, listing my business name and address. I have had excellent response from this.

Most of my retail mailing list has come from asking people to sign my list at craft fairs. My wholesale mailing list of fabric stores was given to me by a woman who self-publishes and markets quilt books (just lucky there).

ALL COOPED UP PATTERNS

Dale Tuttle
450 N. University Ave. #204
Provo, UT 84601-2860
801/375-8199

Established in 1982
Brochure: Free with SASE

10" and 14" Anna Bear with 3" Pocket Bear; Granny's Cat; Grampa's Hound; Bunny Love; The Barnyard Gang; Barnyard Stick-Ups.

ANIMAL CRACKERS PATTERN CO.

Jacqueline M. Wright
and Gregory T. Hicks
5824 Isleta Blvd. SW
Albuquerque, NM 87105-6628
505/873-2806

Established in 1984
Color catalog: $1.50

16" Elephants - Emmie Lou, Eddie, Sheriff Elliott, Farmer Elmer, Miss Ellie, Sudsy the Sailor, Chef Eclair, 22" Mama and 14" Baby Elmo; 16" Butterscotch Bears - Babette and Bruno; Mama and Baby Bunny; Sydney Snake; armadillos; fish; lambs; music boxes.

Jacqueline began making barnyard friends for her beloved niece and nephews and received so many requests from friends that she started selling them. When she started selling at craft fairs, many of her customers asked if patterns were available. "So I decided to make it possible for them to have the pleasure of creating their own keepsake toys," says Jacqueline. Her husband and one-year-old son critique and test each new toy.

Jacqueline Wright, Dollmaker

ANIMAL TRAX

PO Box 265
Upland, CA 91785-0265

Color catalog: $1

29" Rascal the Raccoon; Rameses the Ram; Princess and Little Bit kittens; Whiskers and Wendy, jointed cats; Gwenevere the Goose; hot-air balloons.

Hi...
I'm Grampa's Hound dog. I may not look like it, but I'm very well behaved. I promise not to chew on your tennis shoes, or do other "puppy things". I'll just sit on your sofa (if that's where you put me) and look cute ...... well,

..... I do need my exercise!

You will Need...

1 Yd. fabric for hound
⅛ Yd. fabric for bow
1 lb. poly-fil for bringing your hound to life

Cream or black floss (whichever looks best with your fabric)

2 6½" x 10" pieces of pellon fleece

2 ⅝" black half-round buttons

designed by: Becky Tuttle

.all. .cooped.up.

450 N. UNIVERSITY #204
PROVO, UTAH. 84601

another barnyard pattern

Toodie 14"

E-Z

E-Z BABY BUDS" 7"

Use up those scraps of lace and trim on tiny Sunflower, Rosy and Bluebonnet.

Fast and e-z method for yarn curls and button eyes make up this little charmer. Dress, pinafore, bloomers, hair bow and shoes included.

Missy Moppet 13"

A Calico Cutie!

Pattern includes apron and cap.

E-Z

Stumblina the Ballerina 27"

SOCCER KIDS 18"

Personalize these kids with your own favorite team colors. Features e-z yarn hair methods and button eyes. Socks are designed as part of leg.

E-Z

Socs   **Sara**

She's awkward and lanky with a bandage on her knee but she'll "trip" into your heart!

AT LAST

PO Box 549
Holmdel, NJ 07733

12" mourning dove or quail.

BAJAMA ORIGINALS

1344 Montevideo St.
Placentia, CA 92670-3909

16" and 20" dragon Gretchen; 13" mermaid Marina; 13" Pocahontas; 16" Unicorn; 13" faerie Heather; 13" Jeannie.

BEARS GALORE

Susan M. Ritter-Kay
PO Box 391
Ledgewood, NJ 07852-0391
201/850-9034

Established in 1984
Catalog: $1 (includes
$2 coupon on 1st purchase)

"Ten Minute Teddy"; 10" to 18" button-jointed bears; 6" to 12" Naughty Ladies; custom bears.

BELLSTON ORIGINALS

Maryland Campbell
3025 W. Lupine Ave.
Phoenix, AZ 85029-3255
602/942-7095

Established in 1983
Catalog: $1

17" Maxwell Mouse; 16" Hoppy and Ima Bunny; 9" Hop, Skip and Jump; 14" Bronco; 15" Teddy; 13" Deputy Duck; 15 1/2" Lil Feather and Tom Tom; 7" Baby Buds; 27" Stumblina the Ballerina; 18" Soccer Kids; 13" Missy Moppet; 14" Toodie.

BUCKWHEATS

Nancy S. Lake
200 W. Padonia Road
Timonium, MD 21093-2107
301/252-2646

Established in 1982
Color brochure: $1

20"x17" Canada goose or snow goose; 13"x15" swan; 11"x17" Old Dobbin; 22"x32" moosehead; 15"x10" mallard duck; 14" mouse family; 10" Mouse in Swing; 12"x7" Mouse in Moon; 16" house cat; 24" Claude Hopper; 17" Floppy Bunnies; 24"x18" Embraceable Ewe; 33" Skating Reindeer; 14" leprechaun; 17" elf; 26" Santa; 16" angel.

BY DIANE

Diane M. Babb
1126 Ivon Ave.
Endicott, NY 13760-1431
607/754-0391

Established in 1975
Color catalog: $1.25

10" bison; 12" beaver; 8" otter; 15" woodchuck; 8" mink; 20" dolphin; 14" sperm whale; 12 1/2" penguin; 21" sea lion; 12" seal pup; 16" hippo; 9" elephant; 8" rhinoceros; 19" giraffe; 8 1/2" walking bear; 18" sitting bear; 10" hand puppets (teddy, koala, lamb, panda, etc.); other designs; fabrics, including plush pile (8 colors), long pile (8 colors), short pile (5 colors) and doubled-side suede (4 colors); eyes (6mm to 21mm); noses (10mm to 30mm); joint sets; growlers and squeakers.

 DIANE'S MARKETING TIPS

Always put out the best product you can whether you sell through the mail or at shows or shops. You will put the same effort into finishing a toy no matter what material you use, so add to your profits by using the best materials you can get. It probably will not add that much to the cost, but can add considerably to the price you could charge.

C.A.P. QUILT DESIGNS

5 Yellow Birch Road
Middletown, CT 06457-4947
203/346-7521

Catalog: $1 (deductible
from first order)

Pelican; loon; duck; penguin; teddy bears.

CAB'S TRUNK

Cyndee Stehouwer
639 S. Quincy
Hinsdale, IL 60521-3953

Catalog: $1

4" plaid bear on sled ornament.

CALICO CRITTERS

3212 Storrington Dr.
Tallahassee, FL 32308-2817

Brochure: $.50 and SASE

12" Christmas Mouse or Easter Bunny with 12 holiday outfits; 10" Santa Sock Mouse or Clown Sock Bunny; 15" Griselda Goose.

CAPPEL'S OF DAYTON

2767 Holman St.
Dayton, OH 45439-1633

Color catalog: $2

19" Calico Teddy with five outfits.

CAROLINE

Carol Spence Ickes
PO Box 289
Osage Beach, MO 65065-0289
314/348-2384

Established in 1984

20"x16" Goosey; 19" Randy Rooster; 23" Teddy; 7" to 14" Frogg Family.

Carol has a BFA in fashion design and credits her grandma with teaching her to sew. She has worked as an assistant designer for a tennis-wear manufacturer and as a seamstress for a custom dress shop.

CAT'S WHISKERS

113 Kenway
Rockwall, TX 75087-3535

Information: $1

Christmas ornaments, including calico cat, sheep and reindeer; felt bear, lion and camel.

CHEST CHUMS

Anne P. Petersen
2436 Laguna Dr.
West Jordan, UT 84084-4626
801/566-0580

Established in 1983
Brochure: SASE

15 animal bibs - alligator, bear, beaver, bunny, dog, donkey, elephant, frog, giraffe, kitten, lion, monkey, raccoon, reindeer, whale - that can also be used as diaper bags, book bags, nursery wallhangings, throw pillows, etc.

CHRISTMAS EVERYDAY

Joyce M. Gillis
PO Box 1173
Grand Rapids, MI 49501-1173

Color catalog: $1

16" Princess, horse head; 14" Traveler the Rocking Pony; 17" Christmas Teddy; 13" Mrs. Christmas; 13" reindeer; 15" Jingle Skatin' Santa; 12" Little Red the elf.

COUNTRY COUSIN

Patricia M. Jackson
PO Box 94893
Schaumburg, IL 60194-0893

Established in 1984
Brochure: LSASE

14 1/2" to 16" dressed bears, dogs, pigs, cats and rabbits made from terry towel or robe velour; 10" bear with embroidered face and heart necklace.

"When I was designing the clothes," says Pat, "I asked them if they wanted to wear shoes. They all shouted NO! But they do like their clothes. They are also quite happy with just a ribbon around their necks."

© *Country Cousin*

COUNTRY KITCHEN CREATIONS	18" and 31" Granny or Grampa Mouse.
7625 W. Bluefield Ave. Peoria, AZ 85345-3117	
Information: SASE	

CRANBERRY CREEK	21" Brampton Bear kit or pattern; 20" Prairie Doll pattern.
Diane Carter PO Box 12434 Overland Park, KS 66212-0434 913/381-5931	
Established in 1979 Color brochure: Free	

THE CRICKET FACTORY	10" penguin with muffler and stocking cap; 18" bear.
Lisa Benson PO Box 213 Apple Valley, CA 92307-0061	
Catalog: $1	

Soft Sculpture Kits

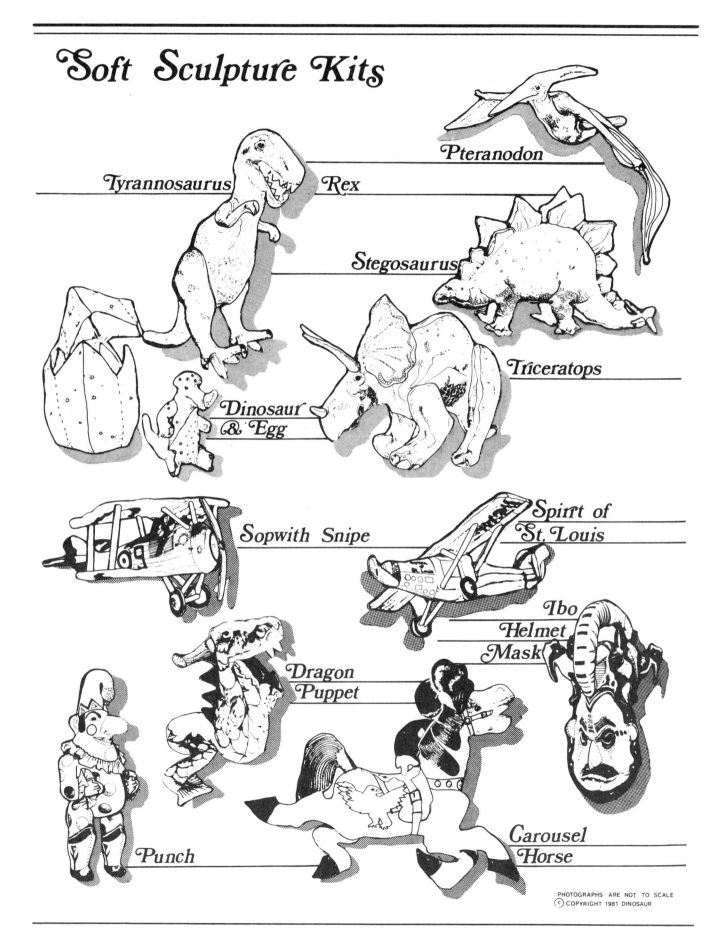

Pteranodon

Tyrannosaurus Rex

Stegosaurus

Triceratops

Dinosaur & Egg

Sopwith Snipe

Spirit of St. Louis

Ibo Helmet Mask

Dragon Puppet

Punch

Carousel Horse

CROSSCREEK

1465 4th St.
Berkeley, CA 94710-1374

Color catalog: $1

Teddykins, including "Rock-a-bye Teddykins Book" and "Holiday Teddykins Book".

D. A. BRINKMANN

Dorothy A. Brinkmann
154 Gordon Drive
Spartanburg, SC 29301-2923

Brochure and photos: $1

4" animals (30 designs, including cats, dogs, squirrel, rabbits, bird, pig, fox, goat, bears, horse, swan, seal, whale, porpoise); 7" to 15" animals.

DILLON'S DOLLS

Jane Dillon
PO Box 2478
Newport News, VA 23602-0478

Brochure: $1

15" Mrs. Santa and Colonial Doorstop Mouse.

DINOSAUR

Michelle and Leonard Lipson
11706 Orebaugh Ave.
Wheaton, MD 20902-2865
301/649-3509

Established in 1975
Brochure: Free

20" Tyrannosaurus Rex; 25" Stegosaurus; 8" Baby Dinosaur and Egg; 9" Dimetrodon; 25" Triceratops; Pteranodon with 50" wing span; airplanes -Sopwith Snipe, Spirit of St. Louis; Dragon Puppet; Ibo Helmet Mask; Tiger Mask; Punch; Carousel Horse.

DIVINE DESIGNS

Cynthia & Bob Safin
Rt. 1, Box 1656
Grayling, MI 49738-9801
517/348-2292

Established in 1981

3" Storybook Mice - Wee Willie Winkie, Halloween Witch, Mom and Babies; Dad in his Top hat.

THE SAFINS' MARKETING TIPS

We have found it best to advertise in the fall and winter issues of craft magazines. It seems that more handwork is done during this time of year.

DIXIE'S LOVE & STUFF

Dixie Stoll
2328 Vernor Road
Lapeer, MI 48446-8315
313/664-5672

Established in 1980
Brochure: $1 or free
with order

14" elephant, 12" horse; 20" fawn; 10" cow and 5" calf; 6" and 10" porker; 15" kitty; 20" newborn baby; 16" baby boy; 24" six-month baby.

DOUBLE D PRODUCTIONS, INC.

Dolores Carlucci
4110 Willow Ridge Road
Douglasville, GA 30135-2750
404/949-3648

Established in 1980
Catalog: $1 (refundable)

19" Pan-Dee Panda; 15" Ko-Dee Koala; 20" Ted-Dee Bear; 11" Dee Dee Duck; 11" Kid-Dee Kitten.

© *Double D Productions, Inc.*

DURELLE ORIGINALS

Durelle Brown
1622 Neptune Lane
Houston, TX 77062-4516
713/480-3365

Established in 1982

© Durelle Originals

"Crusty Critters for Christmas" including Gumbo Joe the Shrimp, Crusty the Crab, Plaid Thad the Armadillo; Tree Top Angel, Christmas Cupid and Mr. S. Claus.

THE EYELET AND LACE CO.

PO Box 15513
Salt Lake City, UT 84115-0513

15" eyelet and lace soft-sculpture swan.

FABRIC FABRICATIONS

PO Box 81173
Salt Lake City, UT 84108-4173

Brochure: $1

12 1/2" Hug-a-Bunny; 17" Farmyard Goose; 19" Canadian Goose; 12" Wooly Lamb; Baby Bear Hug.

FABRIC FUN PATTERNS

Roxi Alderete
PO Box 4354
Fremont, CA 94539-0435
415/656-9403

Established in 1983
Brochure: LSASE

26" Mola Bird; 12" Ladybug and Babies; 19" Chimney Sweep.

"I'm basically a kid at heart," admits Roxi. "I don't think I ever grew out of playing with dolls. When I'm designing a soft creature or character, it's like I'm creating a friend."

Roxi Alderete, Dollmaker

FANTASY CREATIONS

Rebecca Flaming-Martin
PO Box 42374
Portland, OR 97242-0374
503/236-2311

Established in 1984
Brochure: $1

5"x18" baby seal; 6"x13" baby whale; 6"x13" baby dolphin; 8"x19" merhorse; 7"x11" puppy; 7"x11" lamb; 9"x11" or 12"x17" Pegasus/unicorn; 7"x14" rhinoceros; 6"x10" or 16"x20" elephant; 10"x8" puppets (3); 16"x15" Man in the Moon.

Rebecca, who has a BA in English, is a full-time student at Portland Community College where she is studying commercial and graphic arts. "My dream is to be a wealthy businesswoman so that I can support all the causes I believe in," she says.

Rebecca Fleming-Martin, Dollmaker

 ### REBECCA'S MARKETING TIPS

Avoid display ads until you are on your feet. You don't risk as much when you use classified. Expensive classified ads (more than $3 per word) will probably not be cost effective. Keep your ordering information simple. If anyone can misunderstand, they will. There is no need to charge extra postage for Canadians; be sure to require U.S. funds, however. Seek publicity from all media; *never stop* seeking publicity. Find out everything about legal requirements, licenses and safety laws before you invest. Keep good books. Subscribe to trade newspapers and magazines. Use the resources in your library. Don't print your patterns so that your customers have to enlarge or trace any pieces or they will probably not order again. Be sure your instructions are thorough. Plan your advertising months in advance and remember that September through March are the best months for selling kits and patterns. Whenever your customers write to you, take the time to respond. Be professional, but maintain a personal touch.

© Fantasy Creations

FLIGHTSONG

Helen M. Fairfield-Hickey
32 Forest Lane
Millis, MA 02054-1747
617/376-8474

Established in 1984
Brochure: $1 (refundable
with first order)

33 patterns including 14" Walcott Walrus, 23" Dalrymple Dragon, 19" Timmy Toucan, 9' Bothney Boa, 24" Gavin Gull, 24" Baldy Eagle, 24" Murchison Moose, 21" Constance Cow, 25" Chauncey Camel, 21" Torbert Turtle, 19" Prudence Puffin, 24" Millard Monkey; pattern-a-month club.

Helen includes the following paragraph with her original patterns: "What does copyright mean to you? It means you are free to make as many of the animals as you wish for yourself, gifts, or a local fair. You may, also, allow a friend to borrow or copy the pattern for the same purposes. However, no one may reproduce the pattern or make the animals in quantity for widespread distribution for wholesale or retail profit. In other words, don't go into business with them."

© Flightsong

FRIVALS N FRIENDS, INC.

Hilda Adelson
PO Box 801101
Dallas, TX 75380-1101
214/739-2346

Established in 1979
Brochure: $.50

Frivals, including Friliphants, Friligoats, Friluffaloes and Frilicorns; handmade Frivals; polyester fiberfill.

© *Frivals N Friends, Inc.*

GAILLORRAINE ORIGINALS

Gail Jenkins
407 Brentwood Dr.
Tehachapi, CA 93561-2237
805/822-4629

Established in 1979
Catalog: $1

Fully-jointed bears, including 8 1/2" Wee Winkle, 16" Mossy Binkey, 12" Beary Winkle, 15" Isabera, 14" Bumble Bear and Bear Bees, 17" Booger, 13" Longfellow, 10" Tilly, 16" Beeney; non-jointed bears, including 10" Matilda, 20" Granny Bear, 22" Mrs. Rag Bear, 22" Rag Bear, 12" Bear Bear, 12" Pepperrell; pigs, including 20" Lady Yorkshire, 14" Peggy Piggy, 12" Pork Chop; animal babies in drawstring nighties; 12" Bunny O'Hara; 11" Lulu; 12" Mousy; 13" fully-jointed Pussy Willow; 20" Pussley; 10" Mimi; 22" Packy; 24" Doololly the rag floppy doll; eyes and animal eyes (9mm to 18mm); noses (12mm to 25mm); joint sets; fabrics, including fur, fleece, leather, felt.

© *Gaillorraine Originals*

© Gentle Creatures

GENTLE CREATURES

Yvonne La Valle
5045 Mayberry Dr.
Reno, NV 89509-2133
702/747-5419

Established in 1979
Color brochure: $1.50

28" Manjula and Mansi Monsters; 36" Mr. Su the Dragon; 18" Scorpio the Dragon ; 30" Tara Triceratops; 27" Stanley Stegosaurus; 24" Thomas Tyrannosaurus; 13" Plato Pegasus; 14" Uri Unicorn; 16" and 27" Chris Crab and Baby; 16" and 41" Gabriel Gator and Son; 17"x21" Marnie Mermaid; 5" and 13" Sara Whale; 5" and 13" Penny Penguin; 13" Oliver Owl.

GINNY

Virginia Maizenaski
328 Cook Ave.
Middlesex, NJ 08846-2001
201/356-1204

Established in 1982
Information: $.50 and SASE

15" Kathryn and Arthur McBears; 15" Melanie and Ashley Whiskers; 16" Gingham Bear; 9 1/2" Gingham Dog and Calico Cat; 5 3/4" tiny animals (mouse, cat, dog, bear, bunny, pig, elephant); 5 3/4" to 9 3/4" birds (duck, stork, penguin, bird, chick); 7" horse (Pegasus, unicorn, cow, moose, reindeer) and 4 1/2" lamb; 12" Clare and Charlie.

GOLDEN FUN KITS

Berene E. Epp
PO Box 10697
Golden, CO 80401-0600

Established in 1978
Catalog: $1

Animal patterns, including 5" and 13" mama bear and baby, 11" duck, 10 1/2" hen, 14" goose; hand puppet (41 designs) pattern booklets; eyes with lock washers (7mm to 35mm); noses with washers (10mm to 50mm); fabrics, including fake fur (plush, medium pile, lambswool, long pile), cotton, polyester knit, velour; squeakers, criers, growlers; musical movements; sock doll pattern booklets.

Berene started her business when a national crafts magazine, which had purchased one of her patterns, asked about the possibility of selling toy parts to their readers. Today she sells in quantity to toy makers with their own businesses, as well as to home sewers.

THE GRIZZLIES

Laurel Hixson and
Frances Andrews
Rt. 1, Box 410
Elberta, AL 36530-9752
205/962-2500

Established in 1972
Brochure: $.50 (refundable)

12" and 17" fully-jointed bear kits; handmade bears.

Dollmaker Frances Andrews with finished bears.

HEDY HAUKENBERRY

317 Clay
Topeka, KS 66606-1135
913/233-3634

Established in 1984
Brochure with color photo: $1

Cat Family (3 sizes) door stops/pillows, including Draft Cat, with broom straw whiskers and coiled tail.

Hedy is a fiber artist who works at the Secondhand Rose Quilt Shop in Topeka. "I like my work to be functional, as well as delightful to the eye," says Hedy. She lives in a 100-year-old brick house with lots of drafty old doors for her cats to uncoil their tails and help keep out the cold.

HEART AND HAND

Janice Davis
PO Box 1124
El Toro, CA 92630-1124
714/859-0168

Established in 1982
Catalog: $1

13 bears, including Bear on a Stick, 4 1/2" Tiny Ornament Teddy, 9"x12" T. Wheeler Bear, 14" Father Christmas Bear, 10" Lady Edwina and Lord Edward Bear, 16" Little Professor, 17" Jester Teddy, 10" Angel Bear, 13" Victorian Crazy Patch Teddy; Raggs Rabbit, Mr. and Mrs. Hoppington; masonite joint sets.

Jan's students in bear-making class urged her to publish her patterns. "I'm sure they had as little idea of what was involved as I did," she says. About 95% of Jan's sales are wholesale. "One of the hardest things for me to learn about wholesale was to be careful not to price my patterns too low, because you need to allow room for sales commissions, distributor discounts, etc." Her patterns are carried by a local distributor and she has a representative in northern California. "I pay a 15% commission to my rep," says Jan, "and feel it is very worthwhile." Her rep sold $9,000 worth of patterns in 1984. "Finding a good, enthusiastic rep is difficult," she admits, "and I feel I was very lucky. I have tried others who did not work out at all." Jan says her business is at a difficult stage right now because it is almost big enough to require another worker, but not quite big enough to afford one.

HEART FELT FRIENDS

2713 Dunbar Ave.
Ft. Collins, CO 80526-2210

Turtle Dove, French Hen and Partridge in a Pear Tree, Christmas ornaments.

HEART PATCHES

90 S. Wadsworth
Lakewood, CO 80226-1549

14" Heart Paws, baby teddy with three outfits.

HONEY BEE PATTERNS

Sharon Wright
PO Box 91
Jenison, MI 49428-0091

Calico Mouse and Calico Goose doorstops; 44 other designs.

JUDY'S CALICO CUPBOARD

PO Box 56
Moorefield, WV 26836-0056

22" Big Rig truck; 13" Little Chopper helicopter.

KAMISHA AND CO.

Kamisha Malinchak
51 Meadowbrook Road
Randolph, NJ 07869-3808
201/366-4132

Established in 1984
Brochure: $1

18" Christmas Bear; eight 4" Huggers (squirrel, bear, mouse, lion, puppy, kitten, bunny, monkey); eight 4" "Crafts Kids Can Do" (squirrel, bear, mouse, lion, puppy, kitten, bunny, monkey).

Kamisha and her mother, Judy, have their own pattern business. Judy, who has worked for various plush toy manufacturing companies, designs the patterns. I'll let Kamisha explain her duties. "My part is to proofread all the patterns, handle money, test out the patterns and make sure they are easy to understand if you have never made anything like this before. This is a lot to do for a person who is only fourteen," she says. "By the way, my name is Kamisha, but everyone calls me Kami."

KANE ENTERPRISES

Betty Kane
RD 1, Box 398
Narvon, PA 17555-9744
215/445-5307

Established in 1984

5", 9" and 12" Personality Piggs, available in pattern booklet.

 BETTY'S MARKETING TIPS

Do top quality work with good design, good finishing, etc. Sell outright whenever possible and NOT ON CONSIGNMENT! If you DO consign, keep records and get signed receipts for the items you leave. Let the shop owner know you will *not* take back dirty, soiled or damaged work. Remove work not sold promptly. Do your best to be accommodating to customers, but be sure it will be profitable. Always figure your *time* and materials when setting prices. Be sure there is a demand for what you want to make. If a cheap import is available, it *does* limit your sales. Don't downgrade your work - if it is good, believe in it. Learn to analyze what's on the market and what could sell.

Sign your work. If you made it, but did not design it, sew a folded 1/2" name tag into a seam that says "Sewn by _____". If you *designed* the work and have not copied another's ideas or used an existing pattern, use a tag that says "Designed by _____". If your work is completely unique, use a copyright to protect it. You have five years to register the copyright* and it only costs $10. Sewn things are copyrighted, not patented!

*Write the Copyright Office, Library of Congress, Washington D.C. 20559 and ask for copies of application Form TX and Form VA, as well as Circular R1, "The Nuts and Bolts of Copyright".

EXAMINED BY

CHECKED BY

☐ CORRESPONDENCE
Yes

FORM VA

FOR
COPYRIGHT
OFFICE
USE
ONLY

FORM VA
UNITED STATES COPYRIGHT OFFICE

REGISTRATION NUMBER

SHEET.

right Office?

5

VA   VAU

EFFECTIVE DATE OF REGISTRATION

6

See instructions
before completing
this space.

1

Filling Out Application Form VA

Detach and read these instructions before completing this form. Make sure all applicable spaces have been filled in before you return this form.

BASIC INFORMATION

7

2

NOTE

Under the law, the "author" of a "work made for hire" is generally the employer, not the employee (see instructions). For any part of this work that was "made for hire" check "Yes" in the space provided, give the employer (or other person for whom the work was prepared) as "Author" of that part, and leave the space for dates of birth and death blank.

When to Use This Form: Use Form VA for copyright registration of published or unpublished works of the visual arts. This category consists of "pictorial, graphic, or sculptural works," including two-dimensional and three-dimensional works of fine, graphic, and applied art, photographs, prints and art reproductions, maps, globes, charts, technical drawings, diagrams, and models.

What Does Copyright Protect? Copyright in a work of the visual arts protects those pictorial, graphic, or sculptural elements that, either alone or in combination, represent an "original work of authorship." The statute declares: "In no case does copyright protection for an original work of authorship extend to any idea, procedure, process, system, method of operation, concept, principle, or discovery, regardless of the form in which it is described, explained, illustrated, or embodied in such work."

Works of Artistic Craftsmanship and Designs: "Works of artistic craftsmanship" are registrable on Form VA, but the statute makes clear that protection extends to "their form" and not to "their mechanical or utilitarian aspects." The "design of a useful article" is considered copyrightable "only if, and only to the extent that, such design incorporates pictorial, graphic, or sculptural features that can be identified separately from, and are capable of existing independently of, the utilitarian aspects of the article."

Labels and Advertisements: Works prepared for use in connection with the sale or advertisement of goods and services are registrable if they contain "original work of authorship." Use Form VA if the copyrightable material in the work you are registering is mainly pictorial or graphic; use Form TX if it consists mainly of text. NOTE: Words and short phrases such as names, titles, and slogans cannot be protected by copyright, and the same is true of standard symbols, emblems, and other commonly used graphic designs that are in the public domain. When used commercially, material of that sort can sometimes be protected under state laws of unfair competition or under the Federal trademark laws. For information about trademark registration, write to the Commissioner of Patents and Trademarks, Washington, D.C. 20231.

Deposit to Accompany Application: An application for copyright registration must be accompanied by a deposit consisting of copies representing the en-

tire work for which registration is to be made.

Unpublished Work: Deposit one complete copy.

Published Work: Deposit two complete copies of the best edition.

Work First Published Outside the United States: Deposit one complete copy of the first foreign edition.

Contribution to a Collective Work: Deposit one complete copy of the best edition of the collective work.

The Copyright Notice: For published works, the law provides that a copyright notice in a specified form "shall be placed on all publicly distributed copies from which the work can be visually perceived." Use of the copyright notice is the responsibility of the copyright owner and does not require advance permission from the Copyright Office. The required form of the notice for copies generally consists of three elements: (1) the symbol "©", or the word "Copyright," or the abbreviation "Copr."; (2) the year of first publication; and (3) the name of the owner of copyright. For example: "© 1981 Constance Porter." The notice is to be affixed to the copies "in such manner and location as to give reasonable notice of the claim of copyright."

For further information about copyright registration, notice, or special questions relating to copyright problems, write:

Information and Publications Section, LM-455
Copyright Office, Library of Congress, Washington, D.C. 20559

PRIVACY ACT ADVISORY STATEMENT Required by the Privacy Act of 1974 (P.L. 93-579)
The authority for requesting this information is title 17, U.S.C., secs. 409 and 410. Furnishing the requested information is voluntary. But if the information is not furnished, it may be necessary to delay or refuse registration and you may not be entitled to certain relief, remedies, and benefits provided in chapters 4 and 5 of title 17, U.S.C.
The principal uses of the requested information are the establishment and maintenance of a public record and the examination of the application for compliance with legal requirements.
Other routine uses include public inspection and copying, preparation of public indexes, preparation of public catalogs of copyright registrations, and preparation of search reports upon request.
NOTE: No other advisory statement will be given in connection with this application. Please keep this statement and refer to it if we communicate with you regarding this application.

8

Be sure to
give your
daytime phone
◀ number.

LINE-BY-LINE INSTRUCTIONS

9

3
4

See instructions
before completing
this space

1 SPACE 1: Title

Title of This Work: Every work submitted for copyright registration must be given a title to identify that particular work. If the copies of the work bear a title (or an identifying phrase that could serve as a title), transcribe that wording *completely* and *exactly* on the application. Indexing of the registration and future identification of the work will depend on the information you give here.

Previous or Alternative Titles: Complete this space if there are any additional titles for the work under which someone searching for the registration might be likely to look, or under which a document pertaining to the work might be recorded.

Publication as a Contribution: If the work being registered is a contribution to a periodical, serial, or collection, give the title of the contribution in the "Title of This Work" space. Then, in the line headed "Publication as a Contribution," give information about the collective work in which the contribution appeared.

Nature of This Work: Briefly describe the general nature or character of the pictorial, graphic, or sculptural work being registered for copyright. Examples: "Oil Painting"; "Charcoal Drawing"; "Etching"; "Sculpture"; "Map"; "Photograph"; "Scale Model"; "Lithographic Print"; "Jewelry Design"; "Fabric Design."

2 SPACE 2: Author(s)

General Instructions: After reading these instructions, decide who are the "authors" of this work for copyright purposes. Then, unless the work is a "collective work," give the requested information about every "author" who contributed any appreciable amount of copyrightable matter to this version of the work. If you need further space, request additional Continuation Sheets. In the case of a collective work, such as a catalog of paintings or collection of cartoons by various authors, give information about the author of the collec-

tive work as a whole.

Name of Author: The fullest form of the author's name should be given. Unless the work was "made for hire," the individual who actually created the work is its "author." In the case of a work made for hire, the statute provides that "the employer or other person for whom the work was prepared is considered the author."

What is a "Work Made for Hire"? A "work made for hire" is defined as: (1) "a work prepared by an employee within the scope of his or her employment"; or (2) "a work specially ordered or commissioned for use as a contribution to a collective work, as a part of a motion picture or other audiovisual work, as a translation, as a supplementary work, as a compilation, as an instructional text, as a test, as answer material for a test, or as an atlas, if the parties expressly agree in a written instrument signed by them that the work shall be considered a work made for hire." If you have checked "Yes" to indicate that the work was "made for hire," you must give the full legal name of the employer (or other person for whom the work was prepared). You may also include the name of the employee along with the name of the employer (for example: "Elster Publishing Co., employer for hire of John Ferguson").

"Anonymous" or "Pseudonymous" Work: An author's contribution to a work is "anonymous" if that author is not identified on the copies or phonorecords of the work. An author's contribution to a work is "pseudonymous" if that author is identified on the copies or phonorecords under a fictitious name. If the work is "anonymous" you may: (1) leave the line blank; or (2) state "anonymous" on the line; or (3) reveal the author's identity. If the work is "pseudonymous" you may: (1) leave the line blank; or (2) give the pseudonym and identify it as such (for example: "Huntley Haverstock, pseudonym"); or (3) reveal the author's name, making clear which is the real name and which is the pseudonym (for example: "Henry Leek, whose pseudonym is Priam Farrel"). However, the citizenship or domicile of the author **must** be given in all cases.

Dates of Birth and Death: If the author is dead, the statute requires that the year of death be included in the application unless the work is anonymous or pseudonymous. The author's birth date is optional, but is useful as a form of identification. Leave this space blank if the author's contribution was a "work made for hire."

nent filed in

Nov. 1981-600,000

Illustration of the forms needed to register designs for copyright. If you need application forms in a hurry, you may now call (202) 287-9100 at any time, day or night, to leave your request as a recorded message on the Forms "Hotline" of the Copyright Office in Washington, DC.

COPYRIGHTED MATERIAL TIPS

Some people have started business selling handmade products they make, but have not designed, often taking the designs for such products from popular how-to magazines or books. This is not a wise idea, however. You'll recall what I said about designers who sell only "first rights" to a magazine. Even though their design or project may be published in a how-to magazine, they may still retain the exclusive right to sell finished products or kits made from that design. Unfortunately, magazines and designers do not always warn the public in such cases. So, if you plan to sell a considerable quantity of any product you have not designed yourself, you first should obtain permission in writing from the original creator. (You need not be concerned if you only plan to make a couple of things for a church bazaar; it's "going commercial" with someone else's designs that is the problem here.) You always can write to the creator in care of the publisher who issued the book or magazine containing the design.

This kind of copyright violation, sometimes called "pattern piracy," is a matter of growing concern today as an increasing number of craft and hobby consumers unknowingly break copyright laws and thus affect the profits of craftspeople, designers, writers, publishers, and manufacturers. As a result, a growing number of creators are considering lawsuits today. Make sure you don't become "another case for the books."

Now let me give you several specific "copyright no-no's." Pattern piracy and other copyright law violations occur *whenever the copying of something in any way affects the profits or labors of the original author or creator and/or results in profit to the user.* To avoid problems:

1. Do not make for sale any reproductions of such copyrighted characters as Snoopy, Raggedy Ann & Andy, the Sesame Street Gang, or the Walt Disney characters unless you have written permission from the copyright holders to do so. (Commercial patterns or kits of such characters — which have been offered to buyers by licensed manufacturers — can, of course, be made for personal use or gifts. And, unless a magazine, book, or pattern specifically warns against reproduction for profit, the innocent person who makes the handmade item for sale will not be held liable in a court of law.)

2. Do not photocopy — for sale or trade — any pattern, article, or other printed material from any book, magazine, newsletter, etc. which bears a copyright notice. (Such use denies the creator the profit from a copy which might have been sold.) . . .

8. Do not copy, for purposes of resale either as a design or a finished product, the designs on handcrafted products or commercial gift items because all commercial manufacturers and many professional craft designers/sellers protect their work by copyrights or design patents.

Finally, in spite of what you may have heard, it is not all right merely to "change one thing," or use a different color or material. Merely changing the way a design is used does not alter the fact that it is a copy. A work does not have to be identical to the original to be a copy, but only has to repeat a "substantial part" of it, according to The Copyright Office. Unless you can legally define the words, "substantial part," it would be wise to avoid altering commercial patterns for sale as original designs, or selling any handmade object that has been designed by another person.

However, it *is* possible to get your own copyright in a "derivative work." You may need the copyright owner's license and have to pay a royalty, but if it's a new twist on the old and well received, you may still make money — and your own copyright will block those who want to exploit your special new twist.

As you can see, the copyright law is complex indeed. In the end, my best advice may be: *to be safe, be original.*

From *Homemade Money* by Barbara Brabec,
© 1984 by Betterway Publications, Inc.

KC CREATIONS

748 Londonderry
El Paso, TX 79907-4718

Flat Bottom Babies, including 14" cat, 20" rabbit.

KEMA

4683 Everett Road
Richfield, OH 44286

4 1/2" to 5" Christmas mice ornaments, including Mr. and Mrs. Santa, angel, candy cane, nurse, doctor, teacher and jointed Santa.

LEIGHCRAFT

819 Princess Ave.
London, ON
CANADA N5W 3M5

16" Mrs. Marple or Chef Ollie.

LITTLE BROWN HOUSE PATTERNS

Barbara J. Vassler
PO Box 671
Hillsboro, OR 97123-0671

Established in 1982
Brochure: SASE

12" Country Cousins and 14" Farm Boy; 20" Gert and Kermit Bearstreim; Country Quacker; Doll purse; Calico Kitty; Victorian Dove.

 BARBARA'S MARKETING TIPS

Use the best materials available and don't be afraid to price the product accordingly. If you try to make something less expensively with cheap materials, the finished item just looks cheap no matter how much time you've put into it or how good your workmanship is. I have found that a customer is perfectly willing to spend a few dollars for an item if it looks like it's worth it, but will not touch an item that is cheaply priced if it looks cheap.

LITTLE PLEASURES

Margaret James
127 E. LeMarche Ave.
Phoenix, AZ 85022-2502

Henrietta Hippo; Fantasy Ballerina ornaments; 15" soft-sculpture Sleepy Head Angel.

LORNA'S BESTIARY

Sandy Webb
PO Box 2568
Dillon, CO 80435-2568
303/468-8099

Established in 1978
Color catalog: $1

32" duckbilled platypus; 30" baby moose; 24" sloth; 14" muskrat; 15"x40" aardvark; 20"x36" llama, alpaca and endangered vicuna; 20" chameleon; 32" lemur; 20" mother owl and 4" owlets; 14"x22" bear; 20" seahorse and sea colts; 12" toucan; 40" coyote; 12" parrot; 14" beaver; blowfish; 7"x13" armadillo; 38" fish; 10" frog; 7"x23" grasshopper; 9" and 14" cats; 35" jack rabbit; 3" to 6" birds of happiness; 20" turtle; 4" ladybug; 12"x16" chicken; 12" sheep; 9"x15" cow; 20" mother opossum and 6" baby; 19" orangutan; 34" manatee; 17" African elephant and 11" baby; 11"x15" musk-ox; 19" mountain goat and 12" baby; 31" stork; 18" dragon; 21" unicorn and 12" baby; 18" bald eagle; 12"x20" brown pelican; 7"x30" ringtailed cat; 14"x28" sea otter; 24" monk seal; 186" Nessy the Loch Ness monster; 23"x36" harp seal pup; 30" whale; 17" Pegasus; 14" Griffin; 25"x36" camel; rag animals (horse, burro, lion, tiger); hand puppy puppet; 19" troll; 20" mermaid; 21" Centaur; rag dolls.

© Lorna's Bestiary

LUV 'N STUFF

Barb Bullen and Karen Lively
PO Box 85
Poway, CA 92064-0001
Color catalog: $1.25

22" Nickolaus; 11" Treetop Angel; 21" Nicole; 11" Mrs. Mouse; 12" Mama Bear; 10" Santie Mouse; 5" Bunches of Bears; 5" Angel ornaments; 14" Mrs. Bunny; 12" Mrs. Kitty.

M.O.R. ENTERPRISES

12614 NE 140th
Kirkland, WA 98034-1523

18" Jackalope; Buzzy Bear.

A Bearie "Merrie" Ballerina

Perfect ornament, favor or special friend

4½" of bouncy, bright joy!!

Merrie

Materials:
1 dark brown felt square
Felt scraps of: tan, black, white and red
2 - 12" pipe cleaners
Piece of white tulle: 2½" X 72"
1 yd. red 1/16" satin ribbon
½ yd. white 1/16" satin ribbon
Tiny nosegay flowers
Polyfil stuffing

Directions

Full size pattern pieces

1. Cut bear out from felt per instructions on pattern pieces.
2. Using 1/8" seams, stitch around arms and legs, leaving open as indicated. Insert double pipe cleaners into arm; snip at edge; repeat for other arm. Cut remaining amount of pipe cleaners in half; Bend in half and insert into leg (4 thicknesses) and trim at edge as necessary. Repeat for other leg and set aside.
3. Glue eyes, muzzle, nose and white tutu into place per pattern pieces. Glue little red felt hearts to sides of muzzle. Glue white felt ballet slippers to ends of legs. Allow to dry thoroughly.
4. Pinch ears per pattern and baste to front of bear face/body. Pin arms into place and stitch around body using 1/8" seam allowance.
5. Stuff firmly, leaving ¼" at bottom unstuffed. Insert legs, make sure they are even and hand stitch closed.
6. Cut 2 - 1-1/2" long pieces of white 1/16" satin ribbon. Tack to front sides of tutu, across shoulder and to back forming the straps; repeat for other side. Tie 7 tiny bows using 1/16" red satin ribbon. Then tie 1 - red satin bow with 1½" long streamers from each end. Glue bows to top of ballet slippers and also to right facing ear. Set aside other bows.
7. Fold piece of tulle in half to be 2½" X 36". Gather down center lengthwise. Pull gathers and adjust to fit around Merrie's waist. Knot securely.
8. Using 4 remaining red satin bows, glue to ends of straps (front and back):
9. Cut stems off 2 nosegay flowers. Glue one posie right above bow at ear. Using final red bow with streamers, bend tutu down on right side (front). Glue bow so streamers flow onto tutu; Glue nosegay posie right above bow.
10. Adjust legs and arms into dance positions you prefer. Attach gold thread at top of head for ornament.

© 1984 Muffin & Me

Leg- cut 4

Cut above from dark brown felt

arm cut 4

dk. brn. felt

ear-cut 2 Pinch

ear ear

arm bow bow arm

Merrie's head|body

cut 2

leg leg

cut 1 muzzle tan felt

red felt cheeks

Black felt
eye nose
(2) (1)

tutu cut 2- white felt

white felt shoe {2}

MARGIE'S CREATIONS

Margaret L. Coon
1950 Port Cardiff Place
Newport Beach, CA 92660-5415
714/644-4377

3' Missy Mouse and Monsieur Mouse; 3' Bunny Huns and Rodi Rabbit.

© *Margie's Creations*

MUFFIN & ME

Barbara G. Forman
2843 Trenton Way
Ft. Collins, CO 80526-2247
303/223-0255

Established in 1983
Catalog: $1

12" Tree Top Teddy in a quilted skirt; 4" Personality Bears (7 styles); 10" Yule Tide Teddy in wreath; Heavenly Halos ornaments.

NAYELI DESIGN

Antonia Perez
10-28 49th Ave.
Long Island City, NY 11101-5628
718/937-6496

Established in 1983
Brochure: Free

Hand puppets, including Honey Bunny, Ely the Elephant, Lovable Lion, Cuddly Cat, Little Piggy.

PATCH PRESS, INC.

Mark and Sally Harbert
4019 Oakman S.
Salem, OR 97302-2799
503/363-3480

Established in 1978
Brochure: Free

12", 17" and 23" Country Sheep; 8", 10" and 13" Country Fair Pigs; 19" Calico Teddy and six outfits; 15" Teddy Tot and eight outfits; goose door stop; Soft Cradle and 7" Dolly; 26" Drag Around Doll; 13 1/2" jointed Maggie Doll; six soft trucks; 3" Roly-Poly Ornaments (Santa, angel, reindeer, mouse); 28" super Santa; 6" to 12" Christmas Nativity; other designs.

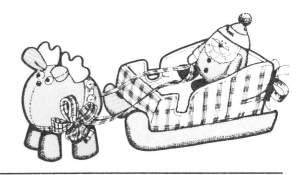

PATTYLOU

Pat Williams
PO Box 996
Jacksonville, OR 97530-0996

Established in 1983
Brochure: $.50 and SASE

7", 9" and 11" Ms. Metilda the Hen; 3", 4" and 5" Mini Metilda.

Pat Williams, Dollmaker

PAULIWOG

Pauli Crandall
Rt. 1, Box 249
Sand Springs, OK 74063-9418
918/242-3289

Established in 1982
Brochure: $1

15" Spring Chicken; 16" Happy Hoppity; 19" Wester Rabbit; 9" Easter Ribbit; 10" Buck E. Beaver; 12" Mama Koala and 5" Tiny; 12" Cali Cat; 13" Fearless; 18" Chimney Deer; 9" Mister and the Missus; 15" Fat Santa; 22" Jingle Deer; 8" Gabriel and Gloria; 10" Sweet Art; 6" to 8" Merry Mini Men; 8" Melody and Harmony; 11" Nutcracker; 12" Ric Rac; 22" Peppermint Andy.

Two of the rooms in Pauli's house are populated with models of soft animals and little folk. Her closets are stuffed with bags of polyester fiberfill and thousands of patterns. Office supplies fill drawers and bolts of fabric line shelves. Files hold thousands of index cards and records. "It's not a hobby," says Pauli, "*Pauliwog* means business."

Her work day focuses on the arrival of the mail carrier. "Even with plenty to finish from the day before," she explains, "curiosity insists that the contents of the new envelopes be revealed." Mondays are big and Tuesdays are slow. Some days are fat with catalogs, promotionals and periodicals and others are deceptively rich with checks. A real bright moment comes with repeat orders or rave notes. "Red heart letters, as I call them," says Pauli, "really are a boost." Disappointment comes in the form of pink slips from the bank, signaling a closed account or insufficient funds. "It's a real downer to the bottom line and the spirits because we try so hard to provide prompt service," she explains. "A courteous reminder seldom brings results."

Pauli's pattern business is similar to many other home-based businesses. She comes up with the ideas, makes the models, draws the patterns and writes up the instructions. She also designs the display ads, brochures and letterhead. Her husband, Fred, helps with the mail, but each envelope is opened with a simple letter opener. Records and addresses are typed with individual file cards kept for each customer's purchase or request. The Crandalls fold the patterns, assemble the kits, apply postage stamps and cart the mail to the post office 20 miles away. Pauli would like to hire help and perhaps buy a computer, but right now she is taking one slow step at a time.

© Pauliwog

PEACHYPIE COUNTRY CRAFTS

PO Box 1099
Bay City, MI 48706-0099

Catalog: $1

12" cat doorstop; 40" Calico Joe, stick horse.

PEAPODS

PO Box 173
Uniontown, OH 44685-0173

Brochure: $.50 and SASE

10" Gnorbert Gnome; 12" Izzy Wizard; 14" Benny Bunny; 14" Igor Beaver; animal arm puppets; character dolls.

PRINTS CHARMING

55 Mountain Blvd.
Warren, NJ 07060-6329

35-page catalog: $2

8"x11" kittens; 6"x9" and 8"x11" Scraps and Snippers.

PUFFS 'N STUFFIN'

PO Box 333
Grandville, MI 49418-0333

Brochure: $1

21" Granny Mouse; Henrietta Chicken broom cover.

R-RENDITIONS

Rosalie J. Evan
PO Box 1919
Garden Grove, CA 92642-1919
714/534-1093

Established in 1984
Brochure: $1 (credited towards 1st order)

23" Marvey Moose; 17" Marky Bear; 17" Eric T. Mouse; 11" Billy Bear and Toddy Bear; 8" Topper Bear; 12" Baby Suzanne; 10" Carol Angel; Peeper Painter and Peeper Painter II, paint-on eye stencils.

RASPBERRY HILL PATCHWORKS

Luella Doss
2277 Edge Wood Dr.
Grafton, WI 53024-9637
414/377-9116

Established in 1979
Catalog: $2

Life-size fowl, including bantam rooster, Rhode Island red hen, American wild turkey, ring-neck pheasant, old grey goose; 4" miniature barnyard fowl (grey goose, bantam rooster, Rhode Island red hen, white duck); life-size loon; miniature common loon, Canadian goose, mallard duck, mute swan; ornaments (lamb, donkey, cow, camel); jack-in-the-box; country primitive doll; 9" American Classic doll series; holiday primitive dolls (man, witch, angel, Santa); other designs.

Luella says her dolls, birds and animals are "very folk in feeling." They have been recognized at the invitational doll show at the Houston Quilt Market and her birds can be seen at the Museum of American Folk Art Gallery Shop in New York.

SAVAGE'S BEASTS

Karen Savage
146 N. 81st St.
Seattle, WA 98103-4204
206/789-7095

Established in 1979
Brochure: Free with SASE

17" unicorn/Pegasus/horse; 38"x42" standing, swooping and crouching dragons; dinosaurs (Brontosaurus, Stegosaurus, Dimetrodon); 28" dolphin/sperm whale/orca; 33" aardvark (with ants); quick creature costumes; 45" Pteranodon/bat; 20" to 25" hippo/rhino/triceratops; 32" armadillo/Glyptodon.

SEW 'N TALE

701 University Village
Salt Lake City, UT 84108-1022

Bertram Bear hand puppet, show script and a simple theater.

THE SEWING CENTIPEDE

PO Box 218
Midway City, CA 92655-0218

Catalog: $1

23" Beary Patch and Bentley, calico bears; 24" Chunkles Clown; life-size Maxwell Macaw; 21" Daffodil and Duncan, kitchen ducks.

SON RISE PUPPET CO.

PO Box 5091
Salem, OR 97304-0091

Brochure: $.50

18" Nan De Bear puppet; 20" Ryan O'Lion puppet; 24" Floyd De Samoyed puppet; 18" Daniel Le Spaniel puppet; 11" and 18" Miss Kit T. puppet; 22" Meadow Bear, 20" Starlite Bear, 16" Miss Kit T., stuffed animals.

SPENCER'S ZOO

Muriel H. Spencer
715 Walnut Dr.
Rio Dell, CA 95562-1426
707/764-3721

Established in 1983
Color brochure: $1
(refundable with order)

Greta Guernsey/Hannah Holstein; Aggie Angus/Heather Hereford; Inclement Wether; Lamb Mae; Doe Rah Me/Yodel Lady Doe; Randy/-Dinah Mite; Poley Anna Penguin and chick; Gordie Ground Hog; Pepper the P.O.A./Patches the Pinto; Copper the Sorrel/Bucko the Buckskin; Little Bit; Travis T. Bear; Acro Bear; Salome Swine; Mr. P; Paloma Palomino/Buddy Bay; fabric (long pile fur, Nubian speckled era fabric, short pile fur, light yellow sherpa); bear joints; growlers; eyes and noses, including 15mm orange eyes for pigs.

When Muriel was younger, she used to paint rodeo windows for extra money, but she got tired of climbing ladders and teetering precariously on them while a cold wind chilled her fingers or a hot sun roasted her head. "When I reached my forties," she says, "I threw up my hands, tottered off the ladder and shouted 'Enough!'" She took refuge at home and started sewing animal patterns, which led to creating her own designs.

Because Muriel is from the country, the animals she knew personally became her models. The real Yodel used to take walks with her family and once even tried swimming with her children! "I think this is what makes my patterns unique," says Muriel. "I have tried to project the real animals' personalities and appearance in pattern form. The animals with cloven hooves have cloven hooves. The ponies look slightly ornery and a little bit unkempt, the way many ponies whose kids have outgrown them look. A local veterinarian gave me pointers on the pig pattern, while his little pig chased me around the pen trying to bite my feet as I tried to draw him."

"My husband coined the phase, 'Spencer's Zoo', rather derisively," says Muriel, "because my children and I had collected so many live animals to share our home. Since I had heard the name so much, it automatically because the business name."

STUFFIT

Helen Hays
PO Box 18432-158
Las Vegas, NV 89114

5" to 18" jointed bears; t-shirts for bears.

SUNNY SIDE UP

PO Box 936
Provo, UT 84603-0936

Color brochure: $1

Bears; bunnys, 21" Roscoe and 17" Bunny Love.

SUSAN HOMECRAFTS

565 Broadway
Cleveland, OH 44146-2772

"Friendly Faces", 15 soft-sculpture faces, including bear, mouse, pig, dog, lamb, lion, monkey, panda, elephant, unicorn, owl, tiger, frog, donkey, penguin, clown, witch, pumpkin.

THE TEDDY BEAR FACTORY

Pat Ryder
7007 S. Ketcham
Bloomington, IN 47401-9228

17" jointed Jonathan.

THAT PATCHWORK PLACE, INC.

Nancy J. Martin
PO Box 118
Bothell, WA 98041-0118
206/483-3313

Established in 1976
Color catalog: $2

16" Jointed Bear, 11" or 15" Jointed Rabbit, 13" or 15" Jointed Pig, 20" Jointed Horse; *Muslin Mummies & Daddies*, pattern booklet featuring 50" Father in Victorian clothing; *This Little Pig*, pattern booklet; *Always Ride a White Horse*, pattern booklet; *Warmest Witches to You*, pattern booklet with soft-sculpture witches and a black cat; Country Collection, including trotter, doll, cats, sheep, ducks, geese, rabbit, cow, pig; Country Collection for Christmas, including 20" Amanda, 18" Kris Kringle; 23" Mouse Folks; 27" Hilda B. Haggley and 12" Cat; 15" Ms. Hen and 6" Chick; 24" Calico Colt; 39" Flora Floozie.

TOMORROW'S TREASURES

Frances E. Fuller
2836 E. Imperial Hwy.
Brea, CA 92621-6714

Color brochure: $1.25

12" Ragtime, rocking horse; 6" and 8" Tiffany and Theodore, jointed bears; 22" dolls; 3" felt bears; 4" Potbelly Gang animals (bear, elephant, cat and rabbit); 7" reindeer.

THE TOY WORKS, INC.

John Gunther
Fiddlers Elbow Road
Middle Falls, NY 12848
518/692-9666

Established in 1974
Color catalog: Free

Silk-screened animal and doll kits based on classic children's fairytales: Edwardian Family, including 10", 14" and 15" cats; Museum Collection, including 22" Dancing Goose, 15" Pug Dog, 14" Humpty Dumpty; Wind in the Willows Collection, including 7 1/2" Toad, 7 1/2" Ratty, 7 1/2" Mr. Badger, 7" Mole; 10" Velveteen Rabbit; Alphabears; 13" Mother Goose characters; handmade items.

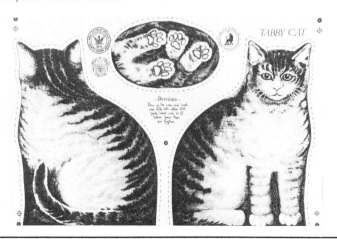

THE TOYLADY

PO Box 503
Dallas, OR 97338-0503

Brochure: $1

10" and 17" Beatrice and Bernie bears; lamb; bunny; Morris the Moose; Pigasus the Flying Pig.

UNIQUE HANDMADE
STUFFED TOYS

Mary Lou Bastian
RFD 1, Box 369
Claremont, NH 03743-9801
603/542-2846

Established in 1979
Information: Free

15"x6" spider; 18" octopus; 27" road runner; 8" oyster; 11" bumble bee; 23" lobster; 22" caterpillar; 8" owl; 14" bunny; 15" alien; 15" Poor Pierre.

Mary Lou's workshop is a backroom upstairs in her house. It's too cold in the winter and too hot in the summer, but she is trying to contain the fuzz from the fur-cutting to one room. "I still manage to track it through the house," she admits. Her three children get to keep the experimental toys that don't come out the way they were planned. "They love them anyway," she says.

VEA PRINTS

Vea Van Kessel
729 Heinz Ave. #2
Berkeley, CA 94710-2739
415/549-0526

Established in 1977
Brochure: Free

5"x8" and 11"x17" cat; 13"x17" pig; 13"x17" sheep; 7 1/2"x 4 1/2" angel doll ornament; 15"x6" Jenny Doll; 4 1/2"x8" Raggedy Ann doll, all silk-screened on natural muslin; handmade dolls.

© Vea Prints

Joan Wooliver
6201 E. Huffman Road
Anchorage, AK 99516-2442
907/345-0553

Established in 1984
Brochure: $1

9" puffin; 12" penguin; 17" musk-ox; 15" hippo; 11" dragon.

Joan made stuffed animals for her daughter each Christmas. "Of course, her little friends liked them so I would make up a few extra," she says. Then friends of the friends started asking to buy them. Customers frequently attach little notes to Joan when they order, telling her about real puffins or musk-oxen seen on trips to Alaska.

 JOAN'S MARKETING TIPS

Don't print 1,000 brochures before checking to make sure all the copy will be easy to read after being folded. Our first brochure was printed length-wise and the price list/order form the opposite way. Customers had to turn the paper as they turned the page. Always put together a 'dry run'. Some timesavers might not save you time. We had access to an automatic folding machine and we went folding crazy. Later, as we were unfolding before we could collate only to fold again, it became obvious the machine had not been a timesaver at all.

CHAPTER
3
Accessories

Dolls and bears need clothes and other things to keep them happy, so this section contains information on 15 companies who offer wardrobes, shoes and hats, umbrellas, glasses, doll beds, carriers and cradles. Many of the companies in the first two chapters offer extensive wardrobes designed for their dolls as well. Since companies are listed only once in this book (with a few exceptions in chapter seven), you should check the individual product listings or the index for additional accessories.

ALASKA CRAFT

Sharon Hamlen
PO Box 11-1102
Anchorage, AK 99506-0011
907/345-1621

Established in 1984
Brochure: Free with SASE

Eskimo clothing patterns for 16" cloth dolls, including parka, kusbuk, mukluks and mittens; husky pup pattern and kit; 6" separating zippers.

Sharon designs and sells patterns from her log home outside of Anchorage. "It is important to me to stay home with my child," she explains. "Although Alaska Craft was meant to be part-time, I've never worked so hard in my life."

 SHARON'S MARKETING TIPS

Read everything you can find and talk to other business owners before you make a commitment to establish a home-based business. Develop your own personal style for selling, but keep these four principles in mind: (1) set the stage with a handshake or a friendly welcome, (2) give a presentation by explaining your product and pointing out its attributes, (3) allow questions and quiet time to consider the purchase and (4) close the sale by explaining how to purchase or order.

BRIAR HOUSE

PO Box 2066
Dublin, CA 94568-0206

"Pak a Kid Pak", pattern for doll carrier with adjustable frontstraps; sleeping bag pattern for 5" to 8" or 12" to 18" dolls.

CAREN'S CRAFTS

Caren Bagley
2560 Sundown Ave.
Salt Lake City, UT 84121-3228

Established in 1982
Brochure: SASE

Patterns for crocheted bonnets and pinafores for 8" and 12" bears; 5", 7" and 9" parasols; Belinda's Bonnet and Hat.

DIANE'S DOLLS

Diane Petty
2112 Jenkins Road
Chattanooga, TN 37421-2719
615/894-5783

Established in 1980
Catalog: $1

Doll shoes (suede boots with laces, various plastic shoes, skating shoe, leather-like boots and shoes, suede and leather tennis shoe); real baby shoes in sizes 0, 1, 2 and 3 (white hi-top, black or white patent with soft soles, rust and white saddle shoes, rust and beige suede boot, suede "squaw" boot); hats (poke bonnets, round top and flat top sailor hats, fancy mesh, straw, lace bonnets, felt derby, white felt sailor, cowboy, black felt tri-corner, black felt topper); umbrella frames; joints; stands for 6" to 24" dolls; patterns, kits and books.

FIVE FINGERS, INC.

Doris Breniser, Gail Baughman
and Betty Baughman
37819 Schoolcraft Ave.
Livonia, MI 48150-1009
313/464-0707

Established in 1982

Knitting patterns for bears and dolls.

This mother, daughter and daughter-in-law effort has produced two knitted bear fashion pattern "booklets" that are available through direct mail and in knitting shops in all 50 states.

JUDY JENNINGS LTD.

Judy Jennings
PO Box 1527
Tustin, CA 92681-1527
714/669-0550

Established in 1977
Brochure: $1

Lucite glasses with brass bows and nose piece, including heart shape (4 1/2" across), Ben Franklin style (1 3/4" and 4"), round (2 3/4"), granny half, sun shades; bear accessory pattern (vest, tie, Santa tie, pinafore, dust cap); clown accessory kit (neck ruffle, pompoms, hat); Woodsey Bear and Rainbow Bear kits (eyes, nose, joints, fur, pattern); handmade 18" jointed Rainbow Bears with leather paws (including clown, sailor, grandma), Woodsey Bears, 23" bears, Sachet Bear, Tooth Beary.

 JUDY'S MARKETING TIPS

Get what you make out in front of as many people as possible. Learn from your customers by listening to them. Go to as many trade shows and craft fairs as possible. Have confidence in your own ideas. Network with other craftspeople.

LYN'S DOLL HOUSE

Lyn Alexander
PO Box 8341
Denver, CO 80201-8341

Established in 1977
Catalog: $1.50

Three pattern books for clothing and accessories for reproduction dolls as well as cloth dolls, including *Toddlers' Togs: 1910-1930*, descriptions of the fashions, fabrics, construction and trimming of this period as well as patterns for 16" cloth toddler twins with a 20-piece wardrobe, *The Doll's Shoemaker*, patterns and instructions for 10 styles in multiple sizes as well as an analysis and history of authentic doll shoes, chapters on selecting patterns, styles and materials, trimming shoes and locating supplies, *The Doll Dressmaker's Guide to Patternmaking*, with details on how to make complete patterns and develop design details; plus individual patterns for shoes, hats and period clothing; shoemaking workshops.

Lyn, the mother of two sons, is a professional dressmaker with a particular interest in historic costume and flat patternmaking. She majored in textiles and clothing at Iowa State University.

Lyn Alexander, Dressmaker

BODY INSTRUCTIONS

Materials: Body fabric (24" of 20" wide fabric), press-on inter-facing. Fiberfill, acrylic yarn, embroidery floss or acrylic paint for face, 4 large bu[...] long pencil with eraser, dry rouge.

Make the body of firm fab[...] minimum stretch such as felt, muslin, or Trigger cloth. [...] ress-on Pellon (not all-bias) to wrong side, matching leng[...] Pellon to crosswise of fabric.

1. Pin pattern to fabr[...] line and grain. Cut out. Transfer markings. (Ma[...] fa[...] by stabbing dressmaker's carbon with a large pin[...] wrong side of under leg and arm only. Mark han[...]

2. Pin and stitch darts [...] and ARMS. Put gathering threads in top of UPPER L[...]S.

3. Pin UPPER and UNDER L[...] Stitch, leaving open above "o"s. Clip curves. Pin foot [...] SO[...] tching symbols. Baste. Stitch. Notch curves. Turn l[...] right side out.

4. Pin UPPER and UNDER ARMS together. Stitch [...] etween "o"s and "X"s. Cut out HAND TEMPLATE. Pin to UPPER [...] tching "X"s. Careful[...] d stitch around template, using tiny[...] back stitch[...] m seam allowance around han[...] to 1[...] lip curves of [...] Turn [...] right side out.

5. [...] B seams of BODY. Put gat[...] ds in hip and [...] ODY BACK as indicated. Pin[...] NT, match-ing [...] easing to fit. Stitch, leaving [...] k open. Clip [...] right side out.

6. S[...] mping fiberfill with eraser en[...] Body shoul[...] not stretched. Compare meas[...] ern as you [...] he clothes will not fit if body i[...] f[...] Leave to [...] eg unstuffed at this time. Stuff [...] ame way. Stuff b[...]

7. Usin[...] u[...] & Carpet thread in a long need[...] w to body, with but[...] leg against dart. Pass thre[...] ro[...] ody to second b[...] on, [...] en back to first button. Rep[...] 2 or [...] es. Tie thread securely. Finish stuffing legs. Close top by hand,

(continued on page 1)

 SEWING DOLL CLOTHES TIPS

There are many tricks to make sewing doll clothes faster and more fun. Most of all, you want to keep your quality high and still cut some of the time that it takes to make them, so that your profits will be better. Remember that your time is worth something, too.

One of the best ways to save time is to organize your fabrics and trims. If your space is limited, you can use an old bookcase to neatly fold and store your fabrics with like colors and coordinating fabrics together. You can use clear plastic shoe boxes for laces, ribbons, buttons, etc. By just glancing at your storage shelf, you can find exactly what you are looking for. Digging in boxes under the bed or sacks in the closet is definitely a waste of time.

Now organize your *thinking*. (This is a little harder for *me*!) You will save time if you make yourself a list of your goals. Just how many of each garment do you want to make? If you list them, you will find it easier to do that extra shopping for needed trims, etc.

You will also save time by making similar garments at the same time. You can cut out up to five dresses, for example, at the same time, by laying the fabric pieces on top of each other. Some people like to do all of their cutting and then do the sewing. That part is up to you.

But if you sew all twelve of those dresses that you want to make, at the same time, you will be able to save lots of time by using the assembly method of sewing.

Finish all the sleeves, gather all the skirts, stitch all the buttonholes. Whatever step comes next, do all twelve dresses at the same time. And if you sew all the girl's clothing at one time and then the boy's, you will save time by having the special trims you need for each out once, not several times. Plan ahead for saving time and frustration.

You can do all the machine sewing first, and save the hand stitching until your favorite TV show is on, when you can sit and relax, so that you will use your time to its best advantage.

Small children have trouble with snaps and buttons, so stitch Velcro into the back for a fast and easier closure.

Knit fabrics do not need as much "finishing" work as woven fabrics, so use a soft knit for nighties, shirts, dresses, etc. A firmer knit for pants looks more professional without the raw edges of woven fabrics.

— from *The Art of Making Doll Clothes that Sell* by Diane-Marie Thorpe, © Mes Petit

MES PETITS
"MY LITTLE ONES"

Diana-Marie Thorpe
PO Box 6746
Kennewick, WA 99336-0640
509/586-9831

Established in 1983
Brochure: $.50

22-piece Premie Layette (fits many 15" to 17" cloth baby dolls), includes patterns for undershirt, cap, diaper shirt, bib, waterproof pants, kimono, diaper cover, night gown, night sacque, footed pajamas, tights, bunting, hooded jacket, diapers, pants, joggers, raglan sleeve romper, t-shirt romper, dress, Christening dress, bonnet and crochet booties; other clothing and accessory patterns; *Shortcuts to Success: The Art of Making Doll Clothes That $ell*, self-published booklet.

 DIANA-MARIE'S MARKETING TIPS

Consider the time you spend sewing to be as valuable as the fabrics and trims you use; don't waste your time sewing with scrap-bag fabrics! Use new, appropriate fabrics and do not be stingy with trims and lace. Baby dolls look the sweetest in pastel prints and solids; never use dark colors or bulky fabrics. Always sew your best and you will sell far more doll clothes. Your dolls will sell better too, if you take the time to dress them well.

NEVADA BEAR CO.

Eloise Page and Vicki Burton
230 N. Mt. View Ave.
Yerington, NV 89447-2238
702/463-3930

Established in 1982
Brochure: $.25

Teddy bear wardrobes, including 10", 13", 16" and 20" overalls, 10", 13", 16" and 20" sundresses, vests, jacket with pants, t-shirts, pajamas and nightgowns, hats with visors; handmade 7 1/2", 13 1/2", 16" and 20" fully-jointed teddy bears.

Eloise and Vicki are a mother-daughter team; Eloise makes handmade bears and daughter Vicki sews clothing for bears.

PRAIRIE PARTNER DESIGNS

PO Box 791
Brookings, SD 57006-0791

Brochure: SASE and $.25
(refundable)

Doll clothes to fit 14 1/2" to 16" cloth body dolls; Teddy Bear Togs, clothes for 14" to 24" bears.

RODA WEE DOLL PATTERNS

Rosalee Aiken
2291 W. Hearn Ave.
Santa Rosa, CA 95407-7377
707/545-1215

Catalog: LSASE

Dress patterns for antique, reproduction and cloth dolls, including Baby Dimples Dress for 16", 18", 20" or 22" doll and Baby Precious Dress for a 23" doll with a 15" waist; handmade dresses.

SWEET DREAM CARRIER

Linda Manuel
PO Box 1505
Ballwin, MO 63022-1505

Pattern for 18" doll basket with mattress, pillow and blanket.

TAILORMAID TOGS FOR TEDDY BEARS

Peggy Meitmann
4037 161st St. SE
Bellevue, WA 98006-1860
206/747-6883

Established in 1984
Brochure: $.25 and LSASE

Apparel for medium-sized teddy bears, including leather aviator jacket with sheepskin collar, knit cuffs and waistband and white crepeback satin scarf, fringed frontier deerskin shirt and coonskin fur cap, fringed deerskin vest, fringed deerskin chaps with lariat, fringed deerskin skirt and bolero, leather sport cap and woolen knickerbockers with matching bow tie and suspenders, leopard print chamois tarzan suit, engineer's cap and overalls (red or engineer's stripe), lederhosen with embroidered band, sheepskin vest, sport vest, backpack in navy or red nylon, deerskin poncho with beads, feather and headband, Santa suit; leather and fur scraps in 1/2 and 3/4 pound bags; needles; *Tips on Sewing Fur*, self-published booklet.

Tailormaid Togs for Teddy Bears is a division of Leathermaids Inc., specialists in custom tailoring of leather and fur since 1968. As a birthday gift, Peggy made a wardrobe for her sister's bear collection. Sis promptly showed them to toy and bear shop owners and a new business was launched.

 PEGGY'S MARKETING TIPS

It is vital to build the image of your business with excellent planning, research and graphics. Your trademark or logo should be sharp and appropriate for your product. Budget enough money for advertising in a well read magazine and/or by direct mail. Thoroughly research your competition and make sure you have a marketable product. Cost accounting is vital - if you are not going to really make a profit, don't try to turn a hobby into a business.

TAILORMAID TOGS FOR TEDDY BEARS

VERLENE'S

Verlene Dawson
PO Box 6113
Spokane, WA 99207-0902
509/484-2097

Established in 1984
Brochure: $1 and LSASE

Doll shoe patterns for 16" dolls (12 styles) and preemies (7 styles); patterns for Sunbonnet Sue and Overall Bill and their clothing; bunny suit; snow suit; bonnet for bouffant hairstyles; six-piece wardrobe for girl preemies,

Although Verlene has been sewing costumes and toys for more than 25 years, she began designing and selling shoe patterns after she read that dollmakers were having difficulty finding shoes for dolls with fat, funny feet. "I had experienced the same problem and had already solved it," she explains, "so it seemed like a good idea to share my pattern." As the mother of a young son, as well as two adult children, Verlene finds it hard to keep the jelly sandwiches away from the paperwork, but she's learned to save those things for the late night and early morning hours. "During the day, I can sew a little. We always take time-out for hugs. He's growing up so fast -my *real live* doll!"

Bunny suit
© *Verlene's*

 VERLENE'S MARKETING TIPS

Read a good book or two about selling crafts. A well-illustrated direct ad is worth more than 1,000 words - people just don't seem to respond to classified ads.

WINDMILL CITY CRADLES

Elizabeth D. Butler
220 Ellen Lane
Batavia, IL 60510-2502
312/879-7679

Established in 1983

Pattern for wood antique doll cradle for 14" doll or bear.

CHAPTER 4 · Materials & Supplies

The 84 companies in this section provide materials and supplies, such as fabric, felt, polyester fiberfill, eyes and noses for dolls, bears and animals, leather, laces and trims, joints sets, hats and millinery supplies.

AIR-LITE SYNTHETICS
MFG., INC.

342 Irwin St.
Pontiac, MI 48053-2399
313/335-8131

Polyester fiberfill; polyester batting.

ALL-FOAM PRODUCTS CO.
INC.

PO Box 128
Morton Grove, IL 60053-0128
312/965-1444

Polyester fiberfill; polyester batting.

ANNE O'BRIEN DOLL
MILLINERY SUPPLIES

Anne B. O'Brien
11208 Tiara St.
North Hollywood, CA
91601-1232
818/763-3934

Established in 1979
Brochure: $1 and SASE

Feathers, including hackle (saddle hackle and jewel tone), goose, coq, marabou, nagoires, ostrich, turkey; flowers (organdy, sheer, sateen, silk), birds (robin, partridge, pheasant, cardinal) and trims (marabou, rose buds) for doll hats; millinery felt (85% wool/15% rayon); 1/8" silk ribbon in 25 colors; straw hats (to fit 4" to 16" head circumference) in 13 colors; 3/16" Swiss hat straw braid; miniature bonnets of Miller's velvet; foundation materials including millinery grade buckram, flex buckram, crinoline; silk millinery wire; 1/4" ribbon wire; wire joiners; hat pins.

ARTIS INC.

PO Box 407
Solvang, CA 93463-0407
800/457-0523

Aleene's Fabric Stiffener; Aleene's Tacky Glue. Idea Sheet #113-"Hats and Bonnets from Doilies and Lace".

BEAR CLAWSET

Marcia L. Campbell
and Suzanne B. Irvin
27 Palermo Walk
Long Beach, CA 90803-4029
213/434-8077

Established in 1982
Brochure: Free

Teddy bear eyes (6mm to 18mm plastic, 9mm to 18mm black button-type, 8mm to 16mm amber glass, 6mm to 14mm black glass); hardboard joint sets (1" to 2 7/8"); plastic joint sets (30mm to 55mm); growlers; plastic noses (15mm to 25mm); felt (50% wool/50% rayon) in 5 colors; calfskin for paws and feet in 8 colors; fur fabric (short pile in 5 colors; shag in 5 colors); music boxes with 18 note movement; needles (3 1/2" to 12"); books and patterns.

THE BEE LEE COMPANY

PO Box 36108
Dallas, TX 75235-1108

Catalog: Free

Snaps in various sizes for doll clothing, as well as the pliers for attaching them.

BERMAN LEATHERCRAFT, INC.

Leather, including chamois, sueded pigskin, calfskin, rabbit skins; leather scraps; leatherworking tools and supplies.

25 Melcher St.
Boston, MA 02210-1599
617/426-0870

Established in 1905
Catalog: $1

BICOR PROCESSING CORP.

Polyester fiberfill; polyester batting; cotton batting.

300 Babylon Turnpike
Roosevelt, NY 11575-2148
516/546-2360

BOYCAN'S CRAFT & ART SUPPLIES

General craft and dollmaking supplies; fabric, including 100% non-running polyester (6 colors) and nylon tubes (3 colors); felt in 22 colors; animal fur in 11 colors; laces and trims; iron-on transfer eyes to fit 12" to 26" dolls; sew-on eyes (10mm to 20mm); animal eyes; lashes; wire glasses; doll hats.

Mail Order Division
PO Box 897
Sharon, PA 16146-0897
412/346-5534

Established in 1952
Catalog: $2 ($1 refundable)

BUFFALO BATT & FELT CORP.

Polyester fiberfill; polyester batting.

3307 Walden Ave.
Depew, NY 14043-2396
716/688-7100

Established in 1916
Brochure: $1
(credited to first order)

BUFFALO FELT PRODUCTS

40% wool/60% rayon 72" felt in 45 colors; custom die-cut shapes.

PO Box 6692
Buffalo, NY 14240-6692
716/847-8566

Color chart: Free

STUFFING TOOLS TIP

Fingers are your first and best stuffing tools, but fingers can't reach into all parts of a casing and they're too clumsy for tiny areas. Knitting needles, crochet hooks, dowels of various sizes, unsharpened pencils, chopsticks, screwdrivers with corners rounded, wooden spoons, skewers, orange sticks, tapestry needles, and even toothpicks are all useful for one job or another.

Choose the tool that fits the size of the cavity to be stuffed, that is strong enough for the job, and that can be held comfortably for a period of time. A long, thin knitting needle will ease stuffing into the tips and corners of long, thin casings, but it will become tiresome to grasp firmly after awhile and it is inadequate when strong pressure is required. The PLATYPUS stuffing tool is surprisingly sturdy, easy to hold, and suitable for pushing stuffing into narrow casings and tricky spaces. Unless carefully handled, any pointed tool can be poked through casing fabric when force is applied. Strong tools with flat, broad tips (e.g., dowels, chopsticks, wooden spoons) are needed when stuffing must be forcefully packed into large cavities.

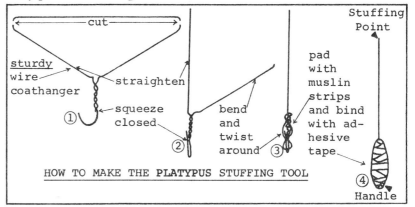

HOW TO MAKE THE **PLATYPUS** STUFFING TOOL

Besides your fingers, the average stuffing project requires more than one tool. Assemble a collection of stuffing tools that you like to use and have them handy when you work. You'll need something long and thin for long, narrow, pointed spaces (e.g., knitting needle, the PLATYPUS stuffing tool); something strong and blunt for large cavities and hard, heavy stuffing (e.g., wooden spoon, thick dowel); something in-between for medium-sized areas when moderate pressure is required (e.g., thin dowel, chopstick). Orange sticks, bamboo skewers, tapestry needles and toothpicks are useful for miniature toys.

— From *The Fine Art of Stuffing* by
Colette Wolff, © 1982 by Colette Wolf.

THE CARRIAGE HOUSE

Rosemary Hanline
1115 W. Outer Dr.
Oak Ridge, TN 37830-8612
615/483-1626

Established in 1980
Brochure: $1 and doubled-stamped LSASE (refundable)

Fabric, including cottons (batiste, broadcloth, lawn, nainsook, prints, checks, organdy, voile), taffetas, satins; French val laces; Swiss embroideries; 3/16" cotton grosgrain ribbons in 6 colors; body broadcloth in natural, pale peach, tan and brown; traditional hair yarn (9 colors) and fluffy hair yarn (9 colors); felt for shoes; sew-on eyes (glass and plastic); specialty needles; mother-of-pearl buttons; fasteners; doll accessories, including shoes (low tie, high button, Mary Jane, laced boot), stockings (cotton tube, diamond pattern tube, rayon tube); straw hats (wide brim, sailor, fashion, Easter bonnet); wigs; stands to fit 6 1/2" to 36" dolls; books and patterns.

CENTRAL SHIPPEE, INC.

46 Star Lake Road
Bloomingdale, NJ 07403-1292
201/838-1121

Established in 1923
Information: Free

40% wool/60% rayon felt (75 colors).

CLEARBROOK WOOLEN SHOP

PO Box 8
Clearbrook, VA 22624-0008

Established in 1939
Brochure: Free

Fabric, including cottons, wools, silks, blends.

CLEARLY COUNTRY

Jiggs Waysack
Elko, NV 89801
702/744-4360

Established in 1983
Price list and swatches:
$2 and LSASE

Fabric, including 100% cottons, muslin, denims, etc.

CR'S CRAFTS

Clarice R. Brown
PO Box 8
Leland, IA 50453-0008
515/567-3652

Established in 1979
Color catalog: $2

Cotton ribbon; dacron/cotton embroidered trim; fabric; fabric fur; eyes; doll shoes (tie, Mary Jane, snap, tennis, buckle, high lace boots, white vinyl, lace, satin baby); socks (rayon and cotton); wigs (braids, pigtails, afro, shag); felt and straw hats; books, patterns and kits.

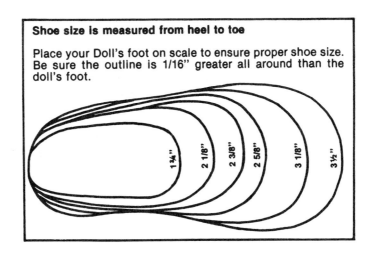

Shoe size is measured from heel to toe

Place your Doll's foot on scale to ensure proper shoe size. Be sure the outline is 1/16" greater all around than the doll's foot.

1 ¾" 2 1/8" 2 3/8" 2 5/8" 3 1/8" 3 ½"

How to measure your doll's shoe size.
Courtesy of CR's Crafts.

THE CRAFTY TEDDY, INC.

Steve Gardner
168 7th St.
Brooklyn, NY 11215-3107
718/768-6005

Established in 1984
Catalog: $1

Fabric, including mohair (3 colors), alpaca (2 colors), Spanish suede (5 colors), imported fur fabric (short and medium long pile in 6 colors); leather for paw pads (4 colors); domestic fur fabric (short and long pile in 9 colors); music box movements; growler voice boxes; squeakers; 4mm to 26mm amber or topaz glass eyes; 3mm to 30mm black plastic button-type eyes; crystal type eyes (8mm to 30mm lock washer and 5mm to 30mm sewing loop); black plastic noses (9mm to 23mm); joint sets (tempered masonite, riveted joint set system, polypropylene); rivet gun; needles (4" curved, 8", 12"); deerskin thimble; stuffing tool; heavy duty nylon thread (7 colors); embroidery floss (4 colors); polyester fiberfill; stands for 8" to 36" bears; patterns for teddy bear frocks, including formal dress suit and top hat, rompers, coveralls, sailor suit, overalls and shirt, dress suit, night shirt and cap, clown suit and hat, safari suit, pants, vest and shirt; felt hats (top hats, derby hats, fedora hats, baseball caps); t-shirts for 10" to 20" bears; ski hats; patterns, kits and books.

ROSEMARY G. CURTIUS

240 Clinton St.
North Fond du Lac, WI
54935-1128
414/921-7463

Established in 1983
Flyer: SASE

Glass teddy bear eyes (4mm to 18mm); 7 1/2" fully-jointed bear and bunny patterns; 6" to 34" fully-jointed handmade bears with humped backs and leather noses.

THE DESIGNERY

Bobbe A. Luce
PO Box 2887
Kalamazoo, MI 49003-2887
616/685-5514

Established in 1978
Brochure: $1 ($.50
credited to first order)

CRAFTags Care Labels, hang tags for handmade dolls and bears.

DIVERSIFIED FOAM PRODUCTS

134 Branch St.
St. Louis, MO 63147-3504
314/231-3340

Polyester fiberfill; polyester batting.

DOLL & CRAFT WORLD, INC.

125 8th St.
Brooklyn, NY 11215-3115
212/768-0887

Established in 1973
Catalog: $3

General craft and dollmaking supplies; shoes; stockings; underwear; wigs; hats; books.

DOLLMAKERS SEWING & CRAFTS

Denise R. Fitko
PO Box 4116
Flint, MI 48504-0116
313/767-0606

Established in 1984
Catalog: $1.25

Fabric, including flannel, cotton, broadcloth, velour, muslin, polyknit; fake fur (short, medium and long pile); shearling fur; 1/4" and 1/2" satin ribbon (9 colors); 3/8" and 5/8" grosgrain ribbon (8 colors); laces; trims; straw and felt hats; buttons and buckles; shoes and boots; eyes; noses; joints.

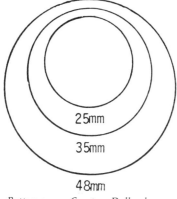

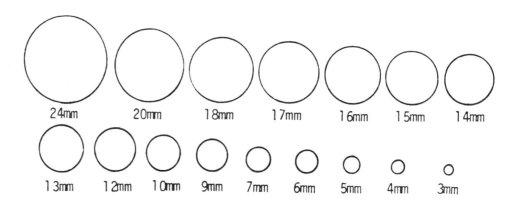

Button gauge. Courtesy Dollmakers.

DOLLS BY CAROLEAN

Carolean Pepmiller
457 W. German
Chester, IL 62233-1324
618/826-4327

Established in 1981
Information: SASE

60" pale pink polyester knit fleece; handmade dolls.

DOLLSPART SUPPLY CO., INC.

5-15 49th Ave.
Long Island City, NY
11101-5610
718/361-1833
2-page color catalog:
Free

General dollmaking supplies; glass eyes; doll stands; shoes; wigs; patterns and books.

FABRICATIONS BY SUZANNE

Suzanne Bourcy
43 Fryling Ave.
Concord, NC 28025-5705

Embroidered eyes (3 styles) to sew or glue on 6" to 26" dolls.

FAIRFIELD PROCESSING CORP.

PO Box 1157
Danbury, CT 06810-1157
203/744-2090

Established in 1942
Brochure: Free with
tax resale number

Polyester fiberfill; cotton/polyester batting; polyester batting.

THE FELTERS CO.

22 West St.
Millbury, MA 01527-2622
617/865-4401

Established in 1909
Price list: Free

Acrylic felt (25 colors); wool felt (37 colors).

FLORIDA SUPPLY HOUSE, INC.

PO Box 847
Bradenton, FL 33506-0847

Established in 1934
Catalog: $1

General craft and dollmaking supplies.

FLUFF 'N' STUFF

Evelyn P. Gray
150 Wareham St.
Middleboro, MA 02346-2403
617/947-2531

Established in 1976
Catalog: $3 ($2 refundable)

Plastic doll joints; iron-on eyes; hats (cowboy, straw, baseball cap, top hat, graduation cap); books.

FOR KIDS ONLY

Pam and Tom Stiegeler
PO Box 1290
Coos Bay, OR 97420-0324
503/269-7158

Established in 1981
Catalog: $.50 and LSASE

"Quickie Curlie" doll hair maker, to make 12" to 22" yarn hair, as well 1/2" to 5 1/2" curls and 3/4" to 12" ringlets; pattern for three styles of booties (mock patent leather, tennis and vinyl cowboy boots) for 18" to 22" dolls.

THE FREED CO.

Leba Freed
PO Box 394
Albuquerque, NM 87103-0394
505/247-9311

Established in 1920

White chamois leather for doll bodies; deerskin, rabbitskin and sheepskin; leather scraps; tiny glass beads for necklaces; handmade Indian dolls.

GOHN BROS.

PO Box 111
Middlebury, IN 46540-0111
219/825-2400

Established in 1900
Catalog: $.25

Fabric, including cottons (flannel, batiste, organdy, lawn, chambray, duck cloth, muslin, terry toweling, denim, quilting prints, percale); notions.

GUTCHEON PATCHWORKS, INC.

Beth and Jeffrey Gutcheon
PO Box 57, Prince Street
Station
New York, NY 10012-0001
212/505-0305

Established in 1975
Price list and fabric
swatches: $2

Fabric, including 100% cotton prints and solids.

HOME-SEW INC.

Bethlehem, PA 18018

Catalog: $.25

Lace; trim; ribbon; buttons; other sewing supplies.

IMPORTS BY CLOTILDE

237 SW 28th St.
Ft. Lauderdale, FL 33315-3131
305/761-8655

Established in 1973
Catalog: $1

Sewing notions, including needles, scissors, fusible interfacings; marking devices and pressing aids; cutting mats; measuring tools, patterns and books.

JOSEPH'S COAT

26 Main St.
Peterborough, NH 03458-2420
603/827-3205

Established in 1980
Catalog: Free

Fabric, including cotton, cotton velveteens, flannels, corduroys.

KEA'S KLOTH

Kealani Davis
PO Box 480
Port Orchard, WA 98366-0480
206/876-4881

Established in 1980
Brochure: SASE

54" velour knit in cream, pale peach and dark brown, available in full bolt (16 yards) and 1/2 bolt (8 yards) only.

KIRCHEN BROS.

PO Box C1016
Skokie, IL 60076-8016
312/676-2692

Established in 1920
Catalog: $1.25

General craft and dollmaking supplies; eyes; eyelashes; felt; craft fur; doll stands; hats.

LEHMAN ENTERPRISES INC.

Don Lehman
RR 2, Box 399
Pound Ridge, NY 10576-9797
914/763-3879

Polyester fiberfill; polyester batting.

MADE WITH LOVE, LTD.

Paulinda Hall and
Patricia Bowling
1832 Young Road
Lithonia, GA 30058-5550
404/981-9579

Established in 1981

Nylon yarn for hair (8 colors); pattern for 10 hairstyles; 3 1/2" needles.

MERRILY SUPPLY CO.

Betty Mednick
8542 Ranchito Ave.
Panorama City, CA 91402
818/341-4931

Established in 1969
Catalog: $2 (refundable)

Music box movements (18 note with winding key), 108 tunes; pull cord music boxes; mini-music boxes, 8 tunes; voice boxes; plastic doll eyes (18mm and 22mm); acrylic doll eyes (8mm to 26mm); oval, half round and fully round glass doll eyes (12mm to 17mm); witch and clown glass eyes (12mm to 18mm); plastic moveable eyes (10mm to 18mm); mohair for wigs; wigs; shoes (German, high-button, Hilda style for wide foot dolls, boy's boots, red vinyl); buttons; hats (flat top, Buster Brown, summer, tennis caps, Kate Greenaway bonnets, pill box); feathers (ostrich plume, hackle, pheasant, mallard duck, Guinea hen, marabou, sand grouse tails); teddy bear eyes and noses; bunny eyes (8mm to 18mm); mice eyes; growlers and squeakers; needles; thread; polyester fiberfill; kapok; excelsior; hardboard washers (3/4" to 6"); cotter pins; steel washers; plastic joint sets (1" to 2 7/8"); fabric, including synthetic fur, nylon velour plush, lamb's wool plush, mohair, alpaca, opossum pelts; felt (3 colors); glasses, including metal frame (1 3/8" to 5" wide), tack-on, sterling silver (2", 3", 4"), acrylic (1 3/4" to 4"), acrylic granny (2 1/2" to 4"); horse hair whiskers; plastic cat eyes (9mm to 18mm); bear patterns; books.

MINI-MAGIC Donna Korb 3675 Reed Road Columbus, OH 43220-4826 614/457-3687 Established in 1975 Catalog: $3	Fabric, including linens, nainsook, cotton net, batistes, lawns, cotton flannel, ultrasuede, peau de soie, sheer woolens, buckram, crinoline, nylon, cottons, broadcloth, silks, taffeta, seersucker, pongee, velveteen; ribbons; buttons; lace; threads; needles; hat making supplies.
NEEDLECRAFT CORP. OF AMERICA 3900 N. Claremont Ave. Chicago, IL 60618-3887 312/583-8800	Polyester fiberfill.
NEWARK DRESSMAKER SUPPLY PO Box 2448 Lehigh Valley, PA 18001-2448 Catalog: Free	Fabric; notions; lace; ribbon; appliques; books.
PELLON CORP. 119 W. 40th St. New York, NY 10018-2505 212/391-6300	Polyester fleece.
POLYART 4670 Interstate Dr. Cincinnati, OH 45246-1110 513/874-5383	Polyester fiberfill; polyester batting.
PRODUCTS UNLIMITED INC. 915 N. 20th Omaha, NE 68102-4319 402/341-2823	Polyester fiberfill; goose down fiberfill; duck feather fiberfill; polyester batting.
PUTNAM CO. INC. PO Box 310 Walworth, WI 53184-0310	Polyester fiberfill; polyester batting.

RANDO MACHINE CORP.

The Commons
Macedon, NY 14502-0614
315/986-2761

Polyester fiberfill; cotton batting; polyester batting.

ROSSCO

PO Box 74
Auburn, WA 98071-0074

Information: SASE

Tiny Ticker, electronic heart implant for dolls and soft animals 16" and larger.

G. SCHOEPFER, INC.

138 W. 31st St.
New York, NY 10001-3401
212/736-6939

Established in 1907

Glass eyes; acrylic eyes.

SEW WHAT FABRICS

2431 Eastern Ave. SE
Grand Rapids, MI 49507-3601
616/245-0834

Established in 1979
Price list and swatches:
$10 (applicable to first
order)

Natural fiber fabric; yarns.

M. SIEGEL CO., INC.

120 Pond St.
Ashland, MA 01721-2098
617/881-5200

Established in 1918
Catalog: $2

Leather, including deerskin, elk, goatskin, calfskin, lambskin; suedes; leathermaking tools and supplies.

STACY FABRICS CORP.

38 Passaic St.
Wood Ridge, NJ 07075-1086
201/779-1121

Polyester fleece.

STANDARD DOLL CO.

23-83 31st St.
Long Island City, NY
11105-2809
718/721-7787

Established in 1922
Color catalog: $3

General dollmaking supplies; wigs; eyes; shoes; clothing and accessories; doll stands; patterns.

THE STEARNS & FOSTER CO.

Williams St. and
Wyoming Ave.
Cincinnati, OH 45215
513/948-5296

Polyester fiberfill; cotton batting; polyester batting.

TAYLOR'S CUTAWAYS & STUFF

James S. Taylor
2802 E. Washington St.
Urbana, IL 61801-4699

Established in 1977
Brochure: $1 (refundable with order)

Fabric scraps and cutaways sold by the pound, including polyester, satin, velvet, velveteen, fake fur, felt, cotton blends; fabric remnants, including polyester and synthetics, satin, double knit, cotton and cotton blends; buttons; lace; patterns and books.

TUMBLEWEED

99 Mt. Auburn St.
Cambridge, MA 02138-4901
617/492-3279

Established in 1974
Catalog and fabric
swatches: $1.75

Fabric, including cotton, cotton blends, unbleached muslin.

UNICORN STUDIOS

Patri Addison
PO Box 370
Seymour, TN 37865-0370
615/573-5941

Catalog: $1
(refundable on first order)

Music box movements, 300 tunes.

THE VERMONT COUNTRY STORE

Weston, VT 05161
802/824-3186

Established in 1945
Catalog: Free

Fabric, including cotton (flannel, sateen, calico, batiste, etc.).

WACCAMAW LINEN

Hwy. 501
Myrtle Beach, SC 29577
803/448-3125

Established in 1977
Catalog: $1

Fabric; yarns; craft supplies.

LUCY WHITE

PO Box 982
Westbrook, CT 06498-0982
203/399-9714

Established in 1977

60" pale peach stretch knit fabric.

YOURS TRULY INC.

PO Box 80218
Atlanta, GA 30366-0218
404/451-9115

Polyester fiberfill; polyester batting.

CHAPTER
5

Handmade Cloth Dolls

If you are a doll collector, or if you don't have time to sew (or can't), the 32 designers in this chapter can provide you with handmade cloth dolls. There is a good variety - clowns, clones and country children, a guardian angel and Mary the Bag Lady, Japanese dolls and Appalachian People, gnomes and Plumpets, a jester and a gypsy.

ANDI'S DOLL NOOK

Andi Leopoldus
4326 W. 4th St. Road
Greeley, CO 80634-1342
303/352-1583

Established in 1980
Brochure: Free

22 1/2" Dress Up Clown; 16" Sleepy Baby; 17" to 20" Oriental dolls; 17" to 25" customized dolls made from washable broadcloth with embroidered and felt faces.

Andi started her dollmaking business when she was pregnant with her second child. "I made a doll to give my three-year-old daughter Missy when she visited the hospital after my son was born," she says. Word spread and soon other pregnant women were asking Andi to make dolls for their kids. That led to doll parties and national publicity in the November 16, 1982 issue of *Woman's Day* magazine. Today Andi has an active mail-order business with local women sewing for her. How does she manage a demanding business and two pre-school age children? "Even my youngest child knows that when I'm in my sewing room, I am seriously at work."

 ANDI'S MARKETING TIPS

Keep overhead low by working at home. Design your own unique patterns. Don't be afraid to convince a few companies that it is to their advantage to supply your small but thriving business with goods at wholesale prices. To get started, market your product to individuals; they have friends and relatives who will see what you have and become interested in turn. Talk to everyone about what you are doing; take every opportunity to speak to groups. Develop a mailing list. Don't try to grow too fast. Don't try to do everything yourself and, above all, choose something you *like* to do.

AUNT LOIS'S DOLLS

Josephine Lois Madigan
1 Illicks Mill Road
Bethlehem, PA 18017-3746
215/691-3887

Established in 1981

10" to 24" dolls in national costume, baby dolls and little girl dolls in period costume; lamb, rabbit, mice, opossum; arm puppets (fox, bear, rabbit, opossum); bears including one dressed as a bee-keeper.

Josephine has been making dolls and stuffed animals for her family and friends since the early 1950s. After retirement in 1980, a niece and nephew encouraged her to try selling at a local craft fair. Sales were moderate at first, but they doubled the second year and, she says, "the home telephone orders at holiday time were very special." Although most of her doll faces are painted with acrylic and can be gently cleaned, Josephine will repaint any that have been "washed or loved off".

 JOSEPHINE'S MARKETING TIPS

When exhibiting at craft fairs, place items at different levels on your display table. Create conversation groups by adding props: a small table set for a tea party or a little bed with slippers peeking out from under a dust ruffle can really draw a crowd.

Josephine Lois Madigan, Dollmaker

JULIE BELOSIC

PO Box 100
Genoa, NV 89411-0100
702/782-5285

Information and photos:
$1.50

15" clowns; 13" tooth fairies with embroidered faces; costumed bears including 2" to 5" miniature bears; stuffed animals.

Julie's home-based business is an extension of a hobby that began by making playthings for her two young children. With encouragement from friends, she started showing her dolls at local craft fairs. "I like to think my work is different from your ordinary plaything because I strive for a whimsical and often one-of-a-kind item that adults as well as children can enjoy," says Julie. Newest members of her soft-sculpture dolls include poseable bears dressed as clowns, ballerinas, cowboys and a bride and groom.

Judy Belosic, Dollmaker, and "friends"

CAROL'S DOLLS

Carol M. Rodine
4708 Barbara Dr.
Minnetonka, MN 55343-8702
612/935-9457

Established in 1980

15" Storybook Dolls, including Red Riding Hood, Cinderella, Hansel and Gretel, Goldilocks and the Three Bears, Snow White, Little Bo Peep, Witches; 12" to 20" machine-washable dolls with embroidered faces.

CLONES BY CURRAN

Mary Curran
PO Box 752
El Cerrito, CA 94530-0752
415/527-0790

Slightly smaller than life-size soft-sculpture clones, including portrait clones, famous clones, clone characters and psyche portrait clones.

Mary designs floppy, lightweight caricatures that "remind you not to take life too seriously." Clones, says Mary, are great gifts for people who talk to themselves, travelers who want the folks at home to remember them, politicians who need to be in several places at once, imaginative persons who have egos expansive enough to overflow the limits of one body and children who can pick them up, curl up in their lap, punch them out and relate to them as they would to a special adult.

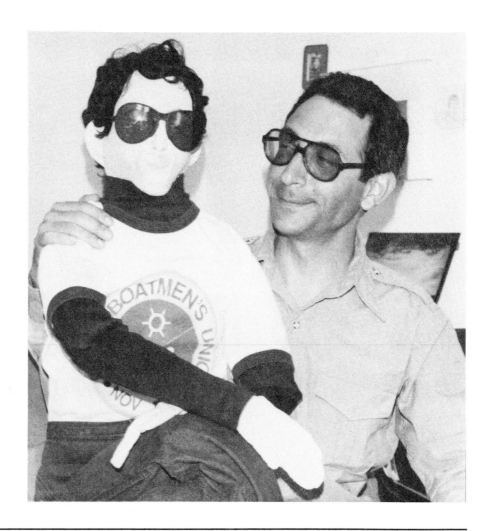

DIXIE'S DOLLS & THINGS

Bess and Sue Dixon
6216 Thornwood Dr.
Alexandria, VA 22310-2961
703/971-5456

Established in 1980
Information: $1 (refundable)

Touch of Country Boy or Girl; four-year-old; bear, rabbit, lamb.

The Dixons are a mother-daughter team who started working together after Sue's graduation from high school in 1980. Bess has four other daughters, but Sue is the one who shares her interest in sewing and handcrafts most strongly. Their dolls are adapted from commercial patterns; McCall's #8967 is the basis for their popular four-year-old.

THE DOLL HOUSE

Bonnie C. Kerr
Rt. 17, Box 605
Cullman, AL 35055-8791
205/796-7830

15" Katrina Ballerina; 15" and 19" Bonnie Baby; clowns.

Bonnie's husband and sons thought the first doll she made was the ugliest thing they had ever seen. But she kept experimenting with cloth dollmaking and today sells award-winning dolls that are signed, dated and numbered. What happened to Doll #1? "We grew to love her," says Bonnie. "She's named Rosebud and my youngest son claims her."

The mother of four sons and one grandson understands that accidents can happen, so she offers hospital and recovery care for her dolls. "Simply write me and explain the ailment," she says. "I will give you an estimate of my fee for corrective surgery, as well as the length of hospital stay. When your baby doll has recovered, she will be rushed back to you via UPS ambulance service."

Bonnie Baby and Katrina Ballerina,
© The Doll House.

Old Fashion Girl, © *Dovic Dolls*

DOLLS

Veryl Marie Worth
PO Box 155
Oakridge, OR 97463-0155
503/782-2703

Established in 1975
Brochure: SASE

Veryl and her husband Harry sell handmade dolls made by other artisans and doll-related books by mail. The Worths also publish *Doll Money Quarterly*, a newsletter for dealers, collectors and dollmakers.

 VERYL'S MARKETING TIPS

Keep the customer in mind at all times. Give them what they want and advertise honestly. Send the product as soon as possible, pack it well and insure the package. Offer 'Satisfaction Guaranteed' and be prompt about refunds. Be interested in the customer's reaction to the product. These practices bring the repeat sales that are the backbone of any mail-order business.

DOLLS BY DOLLINGER

Opal Dollinger
PO Box 221
Toast, NC 27049-0221
919/786-2617

Established in 1984

18" to 26" dolls with handpainted eyes and fabric fur hair; 18" to 20" jointed bears.

Opal worked as a nursing assistant for thirteen years until she began having some problems with osteoporosis. When rib fractures kept her at home, she began to dream of owning a shop filled with her dolls and bears. Her sister, disabled with bone cancer and a dollmaker herself, has encouraged Opal to "go for it".

DOLLS BY FRANCES

Frances Hazmark
Rt. 3, Box 542
Deville, LA 71328-9803
318/466-3196

Established in 1981
Information: $1.50

17" to 23" dolls with embroidered faces; "Much to Do With Socks" and "Hair Dos for All", two self-published booklets.

Frances has been sewing for more than forty years and has made everything from painter's dropcloths to her daughters' wedding dresses. Her dolls are also available as patterns and kits.

DOVIC DOLLS

Dorothy Kohlberg
52 Clinton Hill Road
Wolcott, CT 06716-1011
203/879-0945

Established in 1980

22" Viki.

Dorothy has made about 3,000 dolls in the past twenty years; her husband Vik helps with the cutting and stuffing. Her popular Viki, named after their first grandaughter, was featured in the "Small Business and Crafts" column in the November 1984 issue of *Yankee* magazine. She is made of 100% cotton and stuffed with non-allergenic polyester. "I do not cut corners or use inferior materials," says Dorothy, "because I want my dolls to be passed down to the next generation."

ELLEN TURNER DESIGNS

Ellen Turner
Rt. 1, Box 156
Horse Shoe, NC 28742-9723
704/891-8750

Established in 1977
Color catalog: $1.60

"Appalachian People", Southern Appalachian Mountain Character Dolls, constructed on a wire armature built up with excelsior and cotton padding and then covered with knit fabric.

Ellen, a doll artist and sculptor, has been making dolls and figures for about forty years. Her work has been exhibited at the Renwick Gallery of the Smithsonian Institution in Washington, D.C. and in various galleries and exhibitions throughout the country. She concentrates on presenting the character of the Appalachian mountain region through her dolls instead of simply creating individual figures. Depicting the women of this area is one of her particular interests.

Her parents live in the same rural mountain area of North Carolina where her grandparents lived. Ellen returned to this Appalachian area many times prior to her permanent settlement in 1977. "There are places where you feel completely out of step and then there are others where you flower, prosper and survive," says Ellen. "For me, the expression of the ambiance of the area is the most important aspect. I use the dolls as my medium for this expression. They are not just dolls. They are hill folk with something to say."

 ELLEN'S MARKETING TIPS

For mail-order, you must have a respectable and interesting-looking brochure/catalog and price list. Be dependable and responsible in your business dealings. Shows are great for the contacts and feedback, but you need a well-designed booth. Sell to shops outright and ask for payment before you ship unless you know the shop owner well. Join a respected craft guild.

Sally Bean
Songbird Young'uns
Grandma Ponder
© *Ellen Turner*

FABRIC FOLIO

Mary-Grace Skurka
5429 Claybourne St.
Pittsburgh, PA 15232-1623
412/687-2945

Established in 1985
Brochure: LSASE

10 1/2" self-standing dolls on a round base; Amish dolls; period costume dolls; country animals; specialty bears.

Mary-Grace spent eleven years in New York City as an editor and writer for home-sewing and craft-related publications. She opened a retail fabric shop when she returned to her hometown Pittsburgh but closed it after five years. "I knew I wanted to work more with my hands," she explains. "Instead of giving advice and instruction, I wanted to *make things myself.*" Her dolls - Helene, Gretchen and Marita - are also available as patterns or kits.

GREENBRIER'S DOLLS

Martha L. Rowley
5563 Naiche Road
Columbus, OH 43213-3508
614/866-3213

Established in 1982
Brochure: $1

10" and 16" period fashion dolls with handpainted faces; 16" "Street Scene" dolls, including Mary the Bag Lady.

Martha originally offered only period fashion dolls - May in an 1805 day dress, Frances in an 1860s ball gown, Katherine in an 1870s bustle back gown, Mildred in an 1890s street costume and Elizabeth, a 19th century peddler - but has recently added characters she has met during her years as a social worker in some of the more depressed areas of Columbus.

HOMEMADE HUGGABLES

Mabel Cook
162 Summit Ave.
Phillipsburg, NJ 08865-2453
201/454-7169

Established in 1982

22" muslin dolls with embroidered faces.

A triple fracture of the wrist has slowed Mabel down temporarily, but she expects to build her doll business slowly and on the reputation of quality workmanship. "My soft, huggable dolls are made to withstand the sometimes rough love they receive."

HONEY BEE DOLLS

Diane Stocker
615 N. Buell Ave.
Aurora, IL 60506-3524
312/892-0738

Established in 1983

17" soft-sculpture dolls; 19" ethnic and character dolls; 24" clowns; 16" bears.

Diane sells her dolls through programs sponsored by local community organizations. "I explain different methods of cloth doll construction and include tips on patterns, stuffing, faces, doll clothing and hair techniques," she explains. After the program, Diane sells her handmade dolls or takes special orders.

HUGGIN'S & HANGIN'S

Mary-Ann Bielec
483 27th St.
Niagara Falls, NY 14303-1953
716/284-4023

Established in 1979
Catalog: $1 and LSASE

12" Guardian Angel with removable wings and eyelet-trimmed print dress; 11" Gingerbread Boy; cloth dolls (traditional to punk rockers).

Mary-Ann uses trapunto, silk-screen techniques and a sense of humor to make her fabric creations. Her not-so-angelic Guardian Angel takes off her wings and cotton dress to reveal a voluptuous woman. A green frog pillow pleads "Please don't smoke. I might croak." (Guests won't have to be toad again!) "There is no greater joy for me than the sight of a contagious smile sending a lonely spirit soaring into laughter," says this mother of three.

Mary-Ann Bielec, Dollmaker
"Not-so-angelic" Guardian Angel

LANGE DOLL FACTORY

Katherine Svoboda Lange
Rt. 3, Box 73
Ord, NE 68862-9326
308/728-3127

Established in 1982
Brochure: $1

6" to 22" dolls; 20" Pioneer Prairie Doll; Burlap Bear.

Katherine, the mother of five, has been sewing since she was eight years old. "My pioneer dolls reflect my Nebraska heritage and the storybook dolls show my love of reading these stories to my children," she says. Some of Katherine's dollmaking profits go toward helping abandoned kids in the orphanage in Colombia, South America where her only daughter was adopted. "I make some dolls for her orphanage and send money whenever I can."

Laurie Carlson, Dollmaker

LAURIE CARLSON DOLLS

Laurie Carlson
Rt. 1, Box 75
Deary, ID 83823-9719
208/877-1638

Established in 1981
Brochure: Free with LSASE

26" Country Children, muslin dolls with handpainted faces; 10" Baby Dumplings; 15" Precious Pals; 20" SoftBabies and 30" Toddler Mandy, soft-sculpture dolls; "Sewing and Selling", self-published booklet.

Laurie lives and works on an isolated farm in the wilds of north Idaho with her husband and two pre-adolescent sons. She started designing cloth dolls and toys as a graduate student in the Home Economics department's pre-school at the University of Idaho. Although she also works in porcelain and latex, two of her painted muslin dolls were featured on NBC's *Today* show during the 1984 Presidential Election. Caricatures of President Ronald Reagan and Walter Mondale, designed and made by Laurie, sat on the desk between Bryant Gumbel and Willard Scott on Election Day. Laurie feels sure that this November 6, 1984 publicity was the first time the town of Deary has ever been mentioned on national television.

 LAURIE'S MARKETING TIPS

If you plan to sell through distributors or to stores, you will have to determine a wholesale price. This is the price you will receive from the store's buyer. The store will add a mark-up to it (usually 100% of the wholesale price) to set the retail price — the price it will be sold to customers at. For instance, you may receive a wholesale price of $25, and the store will set the retail price at $50. This may seem unfair to you, but the store has a lot of overhead to cover, as well as making a profit from the sale. You must determine before you deal on a wholesale level what your prices will be, set them so you have a fair return to yourself, then don't worry yourself that the store is getting a profit. You may say, "Gee, I should be selling the doll for $50 myself." Then you must ask yourself where will you get the customers? The store may be better able to reach the customers at that price range than you are.

If you want to go the wholesale route, you will have to market your dolls to the buyers for the stores. You can use such magazines as *Quality Crafts Market* to help you locate these buyers. Approach them with samples or slides of your best work and a brochure of wholesale ordering information. The stores will only be interested in your work if they feel the dolls will sell well when marked up to the full retail price.

— from *Sewing and Selling,* © 1983

© *Laurie Carlson*

© Junko Matsubara Liesfeld

**JUNKO MATSUBARA
LIESFELD**

Rt. 2, Box 175-C
Montpelier, VA 23192-9802
804/883-5244

Established in 1972

3" to 36" Japanese dolls of excelsior and cotton batting with painted features; contemporary dolls.

The Japanese dollmaking masters teach conventional techniques and style, but Junko, a native of Osaka, Japan, rejects this formal training. "I put movement into my dolls," she explains. "They are very free." Junko, mother of three young sons, is also a writer about everyday American life for a Japanese magazine. She and her mother, Toyoko, exhibit their dolls all over the world.

LOU'S DOLL SHOP &
HOSPITAL

Lucille D. Cobb
PO Box 118
Marathon, NY 13803-0118
607/849-6183

Established in 1967

An illness kept Lucille from returning to work, so she started sewing and dressing dolls. She took a course in doll repair and now has the only Doll Hospital in the area. "I had only one doll when I was growing up during the Depression," says Lucille. "I give several doll talks each year to community groups or anyone who will listen."

LUCAS LIMITED EDITIONS

Jean Gibb Lucas
467 N. Lincoln Ave.
Salem, OH 44460-2909
216/332-5634

Established in 1984
Information: SASE

Dolls with painted faces and cotton hair, including 28" Jester in cranberry and navy velour knickers and his own wooden puppet on a stick; 10" Peasant Girl; 10" Newspaper Boy; 10" Boy on a 6" Pony; St. Nicholas; Victorian Girl; hand puppets; animal families.

At the age of four, Jean decided she wanted to be an artist. Her first business effort was in high school when she designed and made silver jewelry. After graduation from college with a major in fine arts, Jean worked as a greeting card designer, a commercial artist and an art director. She began designing and making dolls in 1972 when her third son was born. Fascinated by the three-dimensional human form and its endless possibilities, today Jean keeps busy as a full-time doll artist.

MAMA MAKES EM

Agnes L. Ferguson
10 Fremont St.
Machias, ME 04654-1312
207/255-3607

Established in 1975
Brochure: $1 (refundable
with order)

19" Cappy, boy doll in yellow slicker and so'wester; 28" Allison, Victorian doll; 24" Godey Doll; 20" Rag Bear; 9" Missy Mouse; 14" Christmas Elf; 22 other dolls and animals.

After 22 years of travel, Agnes' husband retired from the U.S. Coast Guard. In a small town in downeast Maine, they bought a large older home with three rooms just for dollmaking. The purchase of an industrial sewing machine made it possible for the Fergusons to develop a wholesale line. They also sell at ten or twelve juried craft shows each year and serve on the Board of Directors of United Maine Craftsmen.

Agnes Ferguson, Dollmaker

The Godey Doll, © *Mama Makes Em.*

MARY WOOTTON ORIGINAL DOLLS

Mary Wootton
1416 Fairridge Dr.
Kingsport, TN 37664-2011
615/245-5874

Established in 1978

12" dolls with handpainted faces.

Mary developed her doll pattern in the 1940s, but didn't have time to mass-produce it while she was raising a daughter and teaching school. Today her home/workshop looks like a miniature garment district with racks of doll clothes and accessories. Except for the snaps and hooks, everything is handmade; each tiny shoe requires nine separate hand operations.

Mary Wootton and "family".

**MIDISLAND CLOTH
DOLL BOUTIQUE**

Winnifred Charette
18 Gillespie St.
Nanaimo, BC
CANADA V9R 4Y3
604/754-1801

Established in 1983

15" to 26" dolls; 12" to 26" rag dolls; animal hand puppets.

Winnifred retired from nursing in 1984 to spend more time making dolls. Since no one is making cloth dolls in her area, there is a big demand for her products at local craft fairs.

 WINNIFRED'S MARKETING TIPS

At craft fairs, give your business card with every sale. People like the idea of knowing where they can get an item in the future if they can't afford it at the moment. Word-of-mouth, however, is the best sales tool.

MISS LIZZI'S

Jennifer J. Walker
2475 Coolidge Ave. #3
Oakland, CA 94601-2637
415/535-1245

Established in 1982

Custom dolls.

Jennifer sells her dolls at the office where she works full-time. "I work on them during my lunch hour," she says. "It seems that people want the doll they actually see you make."

MS. G'S SOFTWORKS

Cabbie Glass
8436 42nd SW
Seattle, WA 98136-2361
206/938-2581

Established in 1976
Brochure: Free with LSASE

16" TinyTown Kids, soft-sculpture dolls.

"I began my dollmaking adventures with enormous enthusiasm, spurred on by an artistic temperament and an innate love of dolls which I had carried with me from childhood," says Cabbie. "The first year or so I spent working with a variety of patterns by several different designers and I read everything I could get my hands on about dollmaking and fabric art in general."

Cabbie, the mother of a young daughter, spent the next three years experimenting and designing, making countless dolls, teddy bears and fabric ornaments. "My ambition at that time was simply to express my creativity in as many forms as I could imagine," she explains. She sold everything she made on consignment to a few local shops. All this experimentation, however, created a number of problems. "It was difficult to promote a business which was constantly introducing new products and phasing out old ones." Not only that, most of her money was tied up in the raw materials needed to produce so many different items.

"I had no production plan," she says. "I merely worked on whatever project happened to inspire me at any given moment." She spent what money she earned as soon as it came in, often stockpiling materials that became obsolete when inspiration led her into new areas. "My time and energies were scattered in a thousand different directions," she admits.

But she learned a lot about design and craftsmanship, cultivating her skills and growing as an artist. "I learned to trust my judgments and to believe in the validity of what I was doing as a designer."

In 1984, Cabbie decided to pursue *one* design idea and stick with it. She gave herself one year to see if she could maintain the discipline it would take to produce only one type of doll. "Happily, I survived!" she says. "Many of the design ideas that came to me during this time did not, however, since I was too preoccupied to do anything about them. Dolls would 'present' themselves to me in visions, crying to be brought to life and I would mercilessly order them back into the realms of my subconscious."

Cabbie sold more than 200 dolls that year and felt a great sense of accomplishment. She did what she set out to do, without compromising her objective of creating dolls of quality or losing interest in her work. "I can now look at the evolution of these dolls and see what a positive transformation they have undergone since I first began making them," says Cabbie. "This would not have been possible had I gone on to something else after a few months."

In the meantime, word-of-mouth contacts have flourished and she is now selling by retail mail-order, as well as on a wholesale basis to shops. She has developed a working production plan, buys supplies wholesale and keeps detailed inventory records. With the advice and encouragement of her husband, who recently completed his MBA, Cabbie has restructured her work environment into a much more cohesive and formal arrangement. Her main focus this year is on production methods, record-keeping (time charts, inventory, financial transactions, etc.) and "creating a sense of order out of the chaos that was my modus operandi for nearly five years."

Has all this organization taken the joy out of dollmaking for Cabbie? "Well, I no longer have the freedom to pursue every design idea that strikes me and I must refrain from impulse buying at the local craft stores. I must discipline myself to the rigors of producing dolls in quantity, rather than working on one doll at a time. Experimentation is at a minimum and time is at a premium," she says. "But I am still surrounded by all the things I love and my workshop is alive with color and the hum of activity. I still feel a rush of pleasure and pride when I finish a batch of dolls and get them ready for delivery."

"I continue to redefine my artistic and business goals as I go," she adds, "and I feel confident that I am progressing along a path of greater maturity in terms of bringing these two areas of my life together."

 CABBIE'S MARKETING TIPS

Craft fairs can be grueling and tedious; sell wholesale to qualified shopowners and maintain personal contact with them. Your work is a reflection of yourself so be conscious of quality. Service is important; go out of your way to please your customers.

Cabbie Glass, Dollmaker and the Tiny Town Kids, © Mrs. G's Softworks.

THE PEOPLE FACTORY

Lisa Lael
12 Merrygrove
Jacksonville, IL 62650-1714
217/243-3754

Established in 1982
Brochure: $1

24" and 30" Home Gnomes - Papa, Mama, Child; 7" Mini Gnomes; 12"x18" "Good Ol' Gals" Pillow Dolls - Nurse Flo on Go; Princeleste and His Frogness; Flora; Catrina and Herba; 19" Kitchen Witch; 25" Tybald the Troll.

Lisa the Gnome-maker received her B.A. in Art Education from Western Illinois University and devoted ten years to teaching. But after reading the book *Gnomes*, she became fascinated with the details of gnome lore. "The need to own a gnome was overwhelming," she says, so Lisa designed a soft-sculpture gnome family, dressed them in felt hats, fur boots and other authentic clothing, and was on her way.

PLUMPET

Joan Polasky
6521 S. 18th St.
Milwaukee, WI 53221-5210
414/761-1036

Established in 1973
Brochure: $.50

20" Plumpets of nylon knit, fabric fur hair and budding wings, including Molly Putz; 8" Pets (Lambkin, Beppo's Pup, Buzzy Bear); 15" puppets (Ginger Rabbit, Fred A. Hare, Big Woods Bear).

Joan, the recreational director for a senior home, is a member of the International Dollmakers' Association. Her dolls, reminiscent of 1920s and 1930s comic dolls, originated in a poem by Christopher Morley, "The Plumpuppets", one of Joan's favorite childhood poems. "It tells of cherubic babies whose job it is to calm children in the night, plump their pillows and blow their noses," says Joan. She began making the dolls for her children in 1973, and soon friends and relatives were asking for them.

Joan is supportive of those who yearn to create their own dolls. "Do some enjoyable homework at your local library - read source books *such as this one*," she advises. "Gobble up patterns and methods offered by the many excellent artists on the scene today. *Then*, don't be hesitant to do your own. We all have favorite characters, whether real or in storybooks, to transform into a doll that no one else has thought of. The world always needs more delight."

© Plumpet

RAINBOW FOG

Rhonda Smith
1546 Van Dyke Ave.
San Francisco, CA 94124-3235
415/822-8816

Established in 1980
Information: SASE

22" cotton dolls with embroidered faces and yarn hair, including Lucy, a gypsy with rainbow-colored hair and eye lashes.

Rhonda is a San Francisco street artist who likes to work with lots of color. She also weaves, crochets and dyes shirts.

© *Rainbow Fog*

Rebecca Iverson, Needlesmith and Kajsa

REBECCA IVERSON *
NEEDLESMITH

Rebecca S. Iverson
Rt. 1, Box 60
Amery, WI 54001-9738

Information & photos: $1

15" to 20" dolls with hand-painted faces - from series such as Victorian Memories, First Recital, Birthday Party, Prairie Flowers, Family Picnic, Christmas Eve, Best Friends, Winter Days; Kajsa, Astrid, Birgitta, Becky; 12" Honey Bear; paper dolls.

Rebecca makes one-of-a-kind dolls and limited editions. Her Honey Bear, with hand-painted leather face and leather footpads, is a limited edition of 100, but most of her series are limited to twelve dolls. Husband Barry, "my most valued critic and mentor," makes wooden accessories for the dolls, such as a slingshot for Huck Finn, a mechanized merry-go-round for a group of bears, an ax for the Tinman and a broom for the Wicked Witch of the West.

Rebecca likes to invite collectors to her home for the one-to-one experience of buying a one-of-a-kind doll. "First we visit my sewing room full of old and new books, photos of children and costumes, baskets of yarns and laces, stacked bolts of cloth and all my latest dolls," she says. "Downstairs in my drawing and painting studio, we look at paper dolls and the beginning sketches for a book. Over cups of tea and something fresh from the oven, we discuss which doll will finally make life complete."

SARAH · BALLERINA
Rebecca Iverson ©1984

MARTHA
·Tiny Dancer.
Rebecca Iverson ©1984

TRADITIONS-
CONTEMPORARY FOLK
CRAFTS

Pamela B. Kline
RD 4, Box 191
Hudson, NY 12534-9804
518/851-9639

Established in 1981
Color catalog: $1

© *Traditions*

16" and 18" Amish Rag Dolls; 10" and 15" Folk Dolls; 16" Shaker Doll; 14" Amos the Amish Teddy Bear; 2 1/2" and 3" Sheep-to-Go; Angel, Bird, Heart and Cat folk ornaments.

Pamela's authentic folk art dolls are available in fine museum shops and galleries across the country. You can see her work in the Folk Art Museum in New York City, the Shaker Museums in Old Chatham, New York and Hancock, Massachusetts, Greenfield Village in Dearborn, Michigan and the Moravian Museum in Winston-Salem, North Carolina.

CHAPTER
6

Handmade Soft Animals & Bears

Handmade bears and soft animals are offered by 56 designers in this section. Although bears predominate, there is plenty of variety in their design and costuming. Animals include handwoven cats, velour dragons and lycra fish.

AMADEUS FAIRY TALES

437 San Mateo Ave.
San Bruno, CA 94066-4415
415/875-9277

Information and photo:
$2 and SASE

18" bear in a 17th century white wig and court costume of powder blue satin velvet and lace, limited edition; other bears.

BASKETS & BEARS

14 Rindge Road
Union, CT 06076-9515
203/974-2106

Brochure: LSASE

Fully-jointed Freeman Bears.

ANNE BEACH

RD 4, Box 534
Halifax, PA 17032-9426

Photos: $1

17" jointed bears made of embroidered linen, crazy quilt, patchwork, white quilted with embroidered heart, signed and numbered; 4" jointed bear.

BEAR BIZ

PO Box 1283
Los Gatos, CA 95031-1283
408/358-2551

Puppet bears; folktale bears.

BEAR EXISTENCE

Merilyn Alexander
PO Box 922
Pasadena, CA 91102-0922
213/449-2893

Handmade bears.

BEAR MINIMUM

Alice McLeod
2765 Sunnyknoll
Berkley, MI 48072-1530
313/542-7425

Established in 1984

2 1/2" bears - clown, sailor, ballerina, angel, superbear, bare bear; 1 1/4" bears.

Alice, a school teacher, makes tiny, jointed teddy bears from scraps of tweed, fabric fur, velour and cotton plaids. Each bear, excluding clothing, has as many as nineteen separate pieces of fabric. "I like small things," says Alice, "and I wanted them to be the right size for a doll house." Her efforts to make smaller and smaller fabric bears have resulted in a fully-jointed and detailed 1 1/4" teddy. She sells her bears through specialty shops and from her home.

Mini bear, shown at three times his size.
© Bear Minimum.

BEAR NECESSITIES

Sandra Larson
PO Box 787
Mt. Shasta, CA 96067-0787
916/926-5027

Established in 1971
Brochure: 1st class stamp

Jointed bears, pandas, rabbits and lambs, made of sheepskin.

Sandra's animals grew out of the heap of scraps left over when she was making skeepskin coats. Now she rarely makes coats, preferring to use her sewing skills to make sturdy stuffed animals. Sandra helped form the Mt. Shasta Artisans Guild which helps local craftspeople learn successful business techniques.

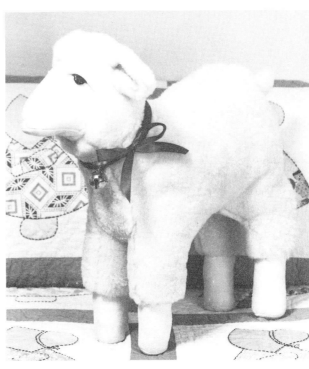

© *Bear Necessities.*

BEAR WITH ME

Cathie Haverkamp
780 Fairway Dr.
Cincinnati, OH 45245-1821
513/753-8173

Established in 1983
Brochure: $1.50

12" to 17" bears, including Bumpershoot, Bride and Groom Bears.

Cathie designs and makes teddy bears from her home; her work schedule revolves around her toddler daughter. "It isn't easy," she admits. Her seven bears have jointed limbs, swivel heads, humpbacks and "growl affectionately when hugged."

BEAR-IN-MIND, INC.

Fran Lewis
20 Beharrell St.
Concord, MA 01742-2962
617/369-1167

Established in 1977
Color catalog: $1

Bears from Gund, Bialosky, Steiff, handcrafted bears; "The Arctophile", quarterly newsletter; sweaters and hats for 20" to 25" bears; T-shirts, tote bags, mugs for bear lovers.

In 1977, Fran and a neighbor borrowed $5,000 to start a mail-order business from their homes. Sales topped $1,000,000 in 1984 but it wasn't an easy journey. Their story is detailed in the November/December 1984 issue of *In Business* magazine. Bear-in-Mind claims to be the first, oldest and largest bear mail-order company in the world and offers this guarantee: "We know how difficult it is to buy by mail, so do return your bear for a full refund if he or she does not get along with you or the other bears in your collection."

BEARS & BIBS

Dot Kunkle
PO Box 691
Downey, CA 90241-0691

Information: SASE

Fully-jointed 24" Bent Leg Bear in red velveteen and white satin robe, jeweled crown and gold leaf scepter, limited edition.

BEARS & BUNNIES

Doris King
409 Main St.
Edmonds, WA 98020-3137
206/775-BEAR

13" jointed bears with shoe button eyes, including Robear, a French painter in muslin smock, Brad the Grad in raccoon coat and a TBU pennant and Bearly Makin' It, wrapped in patchwork quilt and felt bunny slippers.

BEARS & FRIENDS

35106 Date
Yucaipa, CA 92399-3106

Catalog: $1.50

Handmade bears.

BEARS 'N TOYLAND

Suzanne Brockman
2316 Wind River Road
El Cajon, CA 92020-8649

Information: LSASE

15" Miss Holley Beary and Master Nicolas Beary; 13" Little Bobby; other fully-jointed signed and dated bears.

BEARY TRULY YOURS

Kathryn M. Franze
and Susan Johnson
RD 2
Ballston Spa, NY 12020-9802
518/882-6661

Established in 1982
Brochure available

1" to 2" Tiggy Winkles miniature bears; 21" fully-jointed bears.

Sisters Susan and Kathryn had their miniature bears featured on the cover of the March 1983 issue of *Nutshell News* and have been "bearied" ever since. Beary Truly Yours is their own corporate "bearaucracy". Their 21" bear is a limited edition of 1200.

CHARMAINE BREWER

23288 S. Reid Road
Estacada, OR 97023-9418

Photo: $1

11" fully-jointed bears.

CHRISTOPHER BROWN

PO Box 2628
Palm Springs, CA
92263-2628

Information: SASE

Dreamer Bear, Jazzer, Kick-Back, all limited editions.

© Cartier Bear Company

CARTIER BEAR COMPANY

Deri S. Cartier
PO Box 1110
Camas, WA 98607-0110
206/834-6540

Established in 1983

23" Mama and Papa and 17 1/2" Baby Bears; 24" Sweet Country Bear; 16" Rainbow Rusty Bear; 19 1/2" Tuxedo and Thomas cats.

The Deri Cartier bear has close-set, tiny eyes, a distinctive shaved face and curved arms. A clothing and textiles graduate of Washington State University, Deri started making the bears as a gift-giving venture; today she produces and ships 80 to 100 bears each week. She studied and researched live bears before she came up with her own design. "No one wants a bear that looks like the real thing," she explains. "Bears have big teeth and little, mean eyes and long, sharp claws. Make one like that and you'd scare kids out of their growth. But there are things about a bear that people seem to love, the fuzzy hair and the great, round bodies."

CLASSIC CREATIONS

PO Box 3882
Springfield, MO 65808-3882
417/831-7524

Catalog: $1.

Jointed bears and bearwear.

COLLEE BEARS

Colleen Tipton
1825 Forest Ave.
Carlsbad, CA 92008-1017
619/434-3606

Information: LSASE

Collee Bears with the look of the 1900s.

THE CORNER CUPBOARD
OF ZOAR

Anna W. Bachtel
PO Box 627
Zoar, OH 44697-0627
216/874-4559

Established in 1983

ZOARable Bear; cloth dolls, patterns, kits.

After Anna's husband retired, they bought a home in Zoar, a historic community south of Canton. Founded in 1817 by German Separatists seeking religious freedom, the group disbanded in 1898, but their buildings remain. Today the twelve-block historic village features shops, museums, restaurants and restored homes. Syl and Anna own #8 House on the corner of 4th and Park Streets. Their shop features bears and cloth dolls made by Anna, as well as patterns, kits, accessories, counted cross stitch books and supplies. Anna also teaches classes on dollmaking and teddybear construction in the winter and spring; summers are busy with tourists.

Anna Bachtel, Dollmaker

© *Fairy Tale Bears.*

COUNTRY RITZ

Connie Pottroff
1217 Moro
Manhattan, KS 66502-5352
913/539-8209

Established in 1983
Brochure: $1

18" jointed bears; 12"x24" Weathervane Horse; 16" goose; 10" cow; 8" and 12" kitty; 10" lamb; 12" and 16" Mother Goose; 6 1/2" to 16" folk dolls.

D. G. ENTERPRISES

Diane Gard
1005 W. Oak St.
Ft. Collins, CO 80521-2408
303/484-8191

19" fully-jointed Bear With a Heart, limited edition.

FAIRY TALE BEARS

Pat Getchell
1055 Fir Park Lane
Fircrest, WA 98466-5940
206/564-6231

Established in 1984

12" and 17" jointed bears, including Goldie Bear Locks; Snow Whitebear and the Dwarfbears; Old Bear Woman; Little Bo Bear and Lost Lamb Bear; Alice in Bearland.

Pat's Fairy Tale Bears are produced in a limited edition of fifty. Each is signed and numbered.

FAMILY TREE BEARS

3502 Rolling Ter..ace Dr.
Spring, TX 77388-5146

Information: LSASE

Jointed, costumed bears.

FERGUSON RABBITRY

Rt. 1, Box 49
Anna, TX 75003-9704
214/924-3845

13" fully-jointed Joney Bear, made of rabbit pelts.

HuBEARS

Margaret Hubay
341 Westwood Dr.
Woodbury, NJ 08096-3127
609/848-8237

18" Sister HuBear and Brother HuBear.

HUNNEY BEARS

Cynthia Kasper
PO Box 448
Hanover, IN 47243-0448
812/866-3639

Established in 1984
Brochure: Free with
doubled-stamped LSASE

7" to 20" bears; character bears including clown bear, Robin Hood bear and sailor bear.

Cynthia says her bears talk, growl, squeak or sing (via growlers and music boxes). No bear is permitted to leave the Kasper household until it passes inspection by Cynthia's husband William.

© Hunney Bears

JOY TOYS

Joyce P. and
Michael P. Gallo
1024 S. 2nd St.
Moorhead, MN 56560-3353
218/236-6293

Established in 1980.
Brochure: $.50 and SASE

17" machine-washable Teddy Pets, including bear, bunny, cat, dog, elephant, lamb, love, pig, monkey, baby.

Single parent Joyce had to find some way to help support herself and her young daughter when her part-time teaching job was eliminated. "I hoped to find a job with a flexible schedule to allow more time with Amanda. My animals proved to be the answer." Today her family has grown to include husband Michael, daughter Nika and son Bron. The Gallos sell to 125 shops and have three sales representatives as well as two part-time employees. "Life is great," says Joyce. "All that prayer and hard work is paying off. Our toys are truly *Joy Toys*, bringing joy to us as well as to those who buy them."

Dollmaker Joyce Galllo

KENJA DESIGNS

Jane Carlson
139 W. Pershing Ave.
Phoenix, AZ 85029-1814
602/866-8265

Established in 1974

4", 12" and 18" Kinder Cubs; 14" and 16" dolls; patterns.

In 1974, Jane was bored with working at a dead-end job with no future. Then she took a class on dollmaking, made 21 dolls and sold them all through a shop in three days. "I sure didn't want to continue at my job after that, so I gave two-weeks notice and went into the dollmaking business," says Jane. Before long, she was selling at twelve annual craft shows, through seven shops and had five women making doll clothes for her. Her husband was transferred in 1979, again in 1980, and then back to Phoenix in 1981. "If I hadn't liked dollmaking as much as I did, I think I would have quit right then," she says. After a decade of making dolls, however, Jane fell in love with the teddy bear. She uses soft-sculpture techniques to create her Kinder Cubs, complete with tushies, rouged cheeks and freckles.

Jane markets her handmade bear cubs through mail-order and through shops, but she prefers selling at shows. "I like them best of all from a financial standpoint because there is no middleman - you get all the money," she explains.

Jane Carlson, Dollmaker

 JANE'S MARKETING TIPS

For mail-order - carefully choose the magazine that you want for your ad, making sure it is the best possible vehicle for your dollar. Find a good photographer who understands magazine specifications and a reasonably-priced printer who can get the job done when he says he will. Set up your books right away to get all the information needed for future use of your mailing list. Use a good typewriter. Develop your pattern with the utmost care, using plain English that beginners and experts can understand. Use a lot of illustrations. Ask a friend to make up your pattern without help from you. If her results are a close facsimile to yours, you just might have a pattern that will sell. Use a code in your advertising copy to make sure you know where your orders are coming from. If you are unfamiliar with ad layout, have the magazine's ad department lay out the ad or hire an advertising agent. Get your ad and copy in to the magazine *on time.* When your orders come in, keep a good relationship with your customers by answering all questions.

For craft shows - subscribe to a local publication that provides details about area shows such as who to contact, attendance figures, etc. Go to different shows and talk to the craftspeople there; most are very friendly and will share information with you. Don't sign up for "first annual" shows if you are looking for big sales. Check out what the promoters are doing for publicity. If a show is known to be good, don't let a high fee keep you from doing it. Expensive shows can be worth it if you have enough stock to get you through the entire show. A good rule of thumb is that the show fee should be ten percent of gross sales. Follow the rules laid down by the promoter. Tell everyone you know about the show and send postcards to previous customers. Have a neat, interesting display booth with all the supplies you will need. Look interested and be pleasant. Develop a wholesale policy in case shopowners or agents approach you. Be prepared for hard work, lulls throughout the day, a few unpleasant people, loading and unloading and sheer mental and physical tiredness at the end of the show, but most of all - have fun, enjoy the compliments, reap the financial rewards and smile.

For craft shops - check out who you are dealing with. Have a written agreement about consignment or direct sales. Check on how your merchandise is displayed. Know what the store's markup is and don't undersell the shops you sell to if you also do shows. Supply them when you say you will. Remember, this is *your* business, so set the rules at the beginning and stick to them. Keep careful records of what you have at each store.

LASTING TREASURES

Box 647
Rocky Point, NY 11778-0647

Information: SASE

Handcrafted bears; bimonthly newsletter.

LITTLE THINGS

113 Main St.
Irvington, NY 10533-1737
914/591-9150

List: LSASE

1/4" to 3' bears.

LOEBER CATS 84

Judith and James Loeber
517 White House Beach
Millsboro, DE 19966
302/945-2892

Established in 1983
Brochure: LSASE

Handwoven cats with silkscreened, handpainted, embroidered and trapunto faces, made of mohair, brushed wool and various blends; jointed Pussykins, cat dolls lined muslin and dressed in calico; St. Kitty Claus; kittens.

When her toddler daughter wanted a cat, Judith used the leftover peach brushed wool warp to weave her one. "I knew what a real cat would have to endure and, besides, our old dog would never forgive us another intruder," she says. Today, her cats are sold through the mail and at national craft fairs, boutiques and doll shops.

© *Loeber Cats 84*

LUCKY STAR HANDICRAFTS

Bob and Karen Altaras
20551 Hwy. 128
Yorkville, CA 95494-9205
707/895-3542

Color brochure: Free

17" dolphin; 11"x14" toucan; 13" cat; 11" rabbit; 14" dragon; 20" bear; 12"x14" lamb; 17" hippo; 10" floppy dog; 13" penguin; 17" seal; 10"x36" hobby pony; animal crib mobiles.

MAGIC THREADS

Julie McCullough
2026 Ryons
Lincoln, NE 68502-3836
402/475-8560

Established in 1974
Brochure: LSASE

Soft-sculpture dragons, made of velour with metallic or satin stomachs, including 10" baby bean bag dragon; 12" and 22" standing dragons; 12" shoulder dragon; 18" flying dragon; 24" flying sea serpent; exotic birds; Christmas ornaments; mobiles; puppets.

"I have always loved fantasy, fairy tales and mythology so this has a strong influence on my work," says Julie. After seven years as a weaver, she switched to soft sculpture when her pieces became more and more three-dimensional. "My cutting table took the place of my loom and I've been chained to my sewing machine ever since." Julie has a shop at the Kansas City Renaissance Festival each fall and wholesales to shops nationwide. "I have found that fantasy is enjoyed by adults as well as children," she says. "I think it satisfies an inner need for whimsy in our computerized world."

Dollmaker Julie McCullough

© *Magic Threads*

MOONBEAMS

PO Box 6834
Lakeland, FL 33807-6834

12" jointed bear with velvet pads and ears.

NANTUCKET BEARS

Nancy Runyan
PO Box 36024
Phoenix, AZ 85067-6024
602/945-2709

Established in 1984
Brochure: Free

18" to 20" fully-jointed character bears; 18" Minnie and Harry; 17 1/2" Lucille B. and 17" Nettie, her maid; 18" Josiah.

The presence of Nantucket Bears in the deserts of the Southwest often puzzles customers, Nancy admits. "It originated with my grandfather," she explains. "He had nicknames for all his granddaughters and I have always wanted to use mine in some fashion." Nancy's bears are based on her own family history - Minnie and Harry were her maternal grandparents, Lucille was her paternal grandmother, a 1920s radio singer in San Francisco, and Josiah was a Portland banker in the late 1800s.

NOBLE BEARS

Laurel Noble
Box 8662
Rockville, MD 20856-8662
301/770-5909

Established in 1981

6" to 22" jointed bears of mohair, alpaca or fabric fur; Bed Ted.

Photographs of Laurel's bearmaking craft were selected to celebrate women's contributions for Maryland Women's History week in March 1985. "This *Women in the Arts* package will be used in Maryland's schools and libraries," says Laurel, "and hopefully will encourage children in Maryland to pursue a career in the field of arts." Her unique Bed Ted has a removable fur coat and carries his pajamas in a backpack. "Mothers have told me their children feel a real responsibility to get their bear ready for bed and to get him dressed the next morning," says Laurel.

© *Noble Bears*

NOISY CROW ARTISANS

Margaret P. Spoor
99 Beechwood Hills
Newport News, VA 23602-2413
804/877-2228

Established in 1974
Information: $1

5 1/2" to 10" bears; 9 1/2", 13" and 17" muslin Penelope the penny doll dressed in 19th century costume.

"The name of my business stems from a life-long fascination with those intelligent and amusing birds which have such an honorable place in mythology," says Margaret. Most of her designs are based on Victorian toys because she feels that toys of that era were more appealing to children. "The simplicity of their design left so much more scope for imaginative play," she feels. "Soft toys should always be, first and foremost, friend and comforter."

Penelope and bear. © Noisy Crow Artisans

NOSTALGIA BY SYBIL

Sybil Pate
1435 5th St.
Natrona Heights, PA
15065-1204
412/226-3336

Established in 1983

12", 16" and 20" Nostalgia Bears.

A friend once asked Sybil to make her Navy pilot son's jacket into a sentimental bear, complete with helmet, silk scarf and goggles. Then a baby's favorite blanket, a child's pink snowsuit, a discarded lap robe, a woman's evening cape and a golfer's plaid "lucky" pants were all made into Nostalgia Bears. "The response has been outstanding," says Sybil. "Having a memory wrapped up in a bear is so much more fun than having an unworn garment hanging in some dark closet."

PEACEFUL KINGDOM

Lisa S. H. Reitz
c/o Herman's Haven
RR 4, Box 720,
Elm Valley Road
Buchanan, MI 49107-9530

Established in 1981

5" to 23" bears; 8" bunny; 12" elephant; 12" baby harp seal.

Lisa wholesales her dolls and stuffed animals through shops in Michigan and at local art and craft fairs.

PIONEER SHEEPSKIN CO.

Tom and Connie Riter
PO Box 1366
Shelton, WA 98584-0916
206/426-2770

Established in 1966

17" Curly Locks, made of Persian lamb; Walking Bear and Polar Bear; Snow Bear and Silver Bear (2 sizes); 12", 17" and 34" Panda Bear and Teddy Bear.

Tom and Connie have been making sheepskin coats, vests, slippers and rugs since 1966. "But we needed something that wasn't quite so seasonal," says Tom, "so we started making bears." Their bears are made of real sheepskin, with leather paws and noses; each has a leather tag with its own number and date of birth. The Riters sell wholesale and through craft shows.

PLEASANT WALK FOLK

Joyce Sheets
11025 Pleasant Walk Road
Myersville, MD 21773-9222

14" bears with humpbacks, jointed sawdust-filled arms and legs and swivel heads, signed and dated.

PUNKINBEARS

Box 347067
Cleveland, OH 44134-7067

Information: $1
(refundable)

Fully-jointed bears; country bearaphernalia.

RUNNIN' BEAR CO.

Pamela Buckingham
6310 California St. #5
San Francisco, CA
94121-1924
415/387-4004

Established in 1984
Information: Free with SASE

SHASTABEAR

PO Box 384
Mt. Shasta, CA 96067-0384

Brochure: Free with SASE

Fully-jointed bears and rabbits.

VICKIE SOLOMON

111 S. Seminary St.
Napa, CA 94559-3705

List and photo: LSASE

Fully-jointed bears.

SUGAR PLUM BEARS & CO.

Joe and Sheila Adams
317 Hickory St.
Napa, CA 94558-5850

Information and photos:
$1 (refundable)

6" fully-jointed bears; other bears; bunnies.

SWEET TALKER

Dorothy M. Burns
PO Box 19
Lompoc, CA 93438-0019
805/733-4104

Established in 1983
Brochure: $1

12" and 15" bears, including Velveteen Bear, Tuxedo Bear, Blue Jean Bear, Shuttle Bear, Bride Bear, Groom Bear and Ring Bearer Bear.

© *Sweet Talker*

TEDDY BEARS AT HOME

812 Valley Dr.
Duluth, MN 55804-1745
218/728-6200

Mohair bears; accessories including bear quilts and bibs.

TEMPTY BEARS AND TOYS

Pam and Bob Temps
15 Fleming Ave.
San Jose, CA 95127-2451

Established in 1983
Price list and photos: Free with
doubled-stamped LSASE

6" to 16" fully-jointed bears; t-shirts for bears.

TINY TOWN TOYS

Evelyn Parrish
PO Box 115
Cazenovia, WI 53924-0115
608/983-2706

Established in 1984

20" Lovable Leonard the Lion; 12" and 24" thumb-sucker bears; 16" baboon; 22" chimp; 6" elephant; 12" rabbit.

Now that Evelyn's thirteen children are grown, she has more time to sew and make toys. "It gives me such a good feeling to see the children's eyes light up when the animals are finished and ready to cuddle," she says.

TROTTER'S CREEK

Nancy Southerland-Holmes
910 13th St.
Snohomish, WA 98290-1842

11" fully-jointed Honey Bear in tweed cap and tie; Crazy Quilted Teddy Bear, limited edition; *Making Bears* and *Teddy Bears' Wardrobe*, autographed pattern booklets.

WAAS ORIGINALS

4341 NW 3rd Terrace
Pompano Beach, FL
33064-2532

Color photos: $1 and SASE

Jointed bears.

WAINWRIGHT BEARS

PO Box 471
Langley, WA 98260-0471
206/221-3911

8" fully-jointed Teddy Two Shoes with red felt shoes.

NANCY WEIK

Rt. 1, Box 148
Hebron, MD 21830-9774

11" fully-jointed Boo-boo Bear; 14" Pacifier Bear with security blanket.

WHIMSY

Sara J. Little
RD 5, Box 5045
Spring Grove, PA 17362-9106
717/225-4682

Established in 1983

6" to 20" lycra and velour fish with satin fins and tails; 2"x6" soft-sculpture "angel with boobs" tree ornaments; butterflies; bunnies; dolls.

Sara has been working in soft-sculpture since 1977. During a graduate fibers course, she designed and made an old woman doll in a leather bikini, complete with cellulite and high heel studded boots. "I chose Whimsy as my business name since my work always has a touch of humor," says the mother of two.

Sara Little, Dollmaker

CHAPTER 7   Publications, Periodicals & Books

For additional information about making and selling cloth dolls, bears and animals, consult the resources in this section. Included are self-published booklets by the designers, periodicals, how-to pattern booklets and full-length books.

BAREFOOT BOUTIQUE

Gloria Gunther
21205 Golondrina St.
Woodland Hills, CA
91364-5809
818/348-4486

Established in 1983
Color brochure: $1

Tips, Tricks & Timesavers for Cloth Dollmakers, a series of three 32-page self-published booklets; *How to Choose and Use a Vintage Sewing Machine* and *The Delights of Decorative Stitching*, two pamphlets; handmade Mexican costume dolls.

Gloria, a retired teacher who now lives in Mexico because she loves the culture, provides lots of good information in these little booklets, on subjects such as stuffing, faces and contours.

 TINY TIPS FROM GLORIA

1. If you want to remove a pencil mark from cloth, try a clean ERASER instead of attempting to wash out the mark.

2. If some bits of stuffing come up into your embroidery, first try removing the fuzz with masking tape reversed around your fingers. If this doesn't work, insert your needle in under the spot from which the bits of fill are emerging and move from side to side to pull it back under the cloth.

3. If you've considered coating your doll with Scotch Guard to make it stay clean longer, try it out on bits of your thread laid on a scrap of cloth, or on one of your practice heads that you don't care about. Scotch Guard is the acid test of color fastness, and you may be surprised that some excellent brand-name thread will run. The same thread will go through your washing machine with no problem at all.

4. When creating and placing your own doll face, remember that the hairdo will in part determine the position of the eyes in relation to the top and bottom of the head.

— from *Tips, Tricks, & Timesavers for Cloth Dollmakers, Book III,* by Gloria Gunther, © 1983

BEAR-IN-MIND, INC.

(see Chapter 6)

The Arctophile, a quarterly newsletter, established in 1983, for the discerning collector of new bears.

BETTINA'S DOLL DESIGNS

Elizabeth E. Fahr
2509 N. Campbell Ave.
Tucson, AZ 85719-3362
602/325-5364

Established in 1976
Brochure with color
photo: $1.50

Elizabeth Fahr, Dollmaker
Trevor and Trina © Bettina's Doll Designs

Creating Your Own Molded Felt Dolls, a 76-page illustrated self-published book; felt dollmaking kits.

COIFFURES

Thelma Garrison and
Mona Phillips
PO Box 490
Pine Grove, CA 95665-0490
209/296-4407 or
209/296-4339

Established in 1981

© R. Phillips and T. Garrison

Coiffures: Yarn Hair Dos for Cloth Dolls, an 11-page self-published booklet featuring 12 hair styles; 18" sleepy baby and 24" doll patterns.

fig 1

24" to 36"

SHORT & CURLEY

1. Cut a long 2" strip
   of paper.(varies with
   doll size). Fold yarn
   over & over on paper.
   Machine stitch down
   center, folding & stitching as you go(fig 1).
   Doublestitch for strength.

Remove paper. Handstitch to
head in a circular fashion
about ½" apart until head
is covered.

HELPFUL TIPS FOR DOLL COIFFURES

1. Rug yarn or 4 ply yarn is great, but you may want to experiment with others.

2. When sewing yarn on paper, wax paper or newspaper will tear away more easily.

3. Tack or glue straight hair that won't stay in place with a thin strip of white glue. Lift yarn and apply glue with a brush. Press in place with fingers.

4. In making baked curls, be sure to wind yarn on a metal object.

5. Use matching yarn to tie braids or pony tails. Tie ribbons over the yarn ties.

6. For very small dolls, tapestry or cotton yarn (not crochet thread) is good for hair.

7. A round piece of fake fur may be cut to size and stitched by hand for an alternate doll wig.

— from *Coiffures: Yarn Hair Dos for Cloth Dolls,* by Thelma Garrison and Mona Phillips, © 1982

COSTUME QUARTERLY FOR DOLL COLLECTORS

May Wenzel and
Helen Barglebaugh
38 Middlesex Dr.
Brentwood, MO 63144-1031
314/991-3278

Established in 1974

Costume Quarterly for Doll Collectors, a quarterly publication primarily for those interested in making clothing for antique and reproduction dolls.

DOLL MONEY QUARTERLY

(see DOLLS, Chapter 5)

A quarterly newsletter for dealers, collectors and dollmakers.

DOLLS BY FRANCES

(see Chapter 5)

Much to Do With Socks and *Hair Dos for All*, two self-published booklets.

FIDY FERRARA'S DOLL WORLD

Phyllis Ferrara
Rt. 1, Box 365
Forest Grove, OR 97116-9750
503/357-9302

Established in 1982

Fidy Ferrara's Doll World, a bimonthly homespun newsletter, produced and edited by "Fidy" Ferrara who admits to owning 1200 dolls!

CATHERINE FISCHER

PO Box 9051
Pittsburgh, PA 15224-0051
412/441-4577

Established in 1980

Over 100 Doll Faces Suitable for Both Painting and Embroidery, a self-published booklet.

"So many dolls have a plain smile," observes Catherine, "that I couldn't help but think about all the other moods and emotions. Why not have a shy face, or a tired one, a surprised or a self-confident grin, a look of coyness or pensiveness?" So Catherine drew 104 simple line drawings and put them into a small copyright-free booklet. "If it just makes somebody *try* a new face on their next doll instead of the same old smile, it will be successful," she says.

Mix techniques for a unique face. Try painted eyes with a sewn mouth for instance

LAURIE CARLSON DOLLS

(see Chapter 5)

Sewing & Selling, a 42-page self-published booklet written by Laurie Carlson, is packed with helpful information for the inexperienced dollmaker who wants to sell her handmade creations.

© *Laurie Carlson Dolls.*

 LAURIE'S PHOTOGRAPHY TIPS

When photographing your dolls yourself, choose a surface that is about waist-high (like a table top) and find a covering for it that won't look wrinkly in the photo. Velvets, velours, and similar drapeable fabrics work well. Keep the background simple. If you want the doll to show up well in the photo, think in terms of contrast of values. This means light against dark, or dark against light. If your doll is "light" — having light colored clothing and hair, place her against a darker background. If the doll's hair and clothing are dark, they will stand out better against a light colored background. Light colored dolls placed against a black velvet background will seem to "float" — they do show up very well.

Use doll stands or pin the dolls in position as you pose them for the camera. Try to create a lively look to the doll, not a "mug shot". Pose the doll at different angles. Place toys or other small items with the dolls to create a scene. If you want to put several dolls in the same photograph, put a box under the table cloth to create a pedestal and raise the level of those in the back a little.

If you want to be able to list the dolls on a separate price list, number them by placing a small square of paper with a clear black number on it by each doll's foot, or pinned to her clothing. These will show up in the photograph and you can number and describe each on a separate sheet of paper, referring to Doll #3, rather than "the blonde in the sunsuit."

— from *Sewing and Selling* by Laurie Carlson,
© 1983

LYN'S DOLL HOUSE

(see Chapter 3)

The Doll's Shoemaker, The Doll Dressmaker's Guide to Patternmaking and *Toddlers' Togs: 1910-1930*, three extremely well written self-published books written by Lyn Alexander, primarily for dressing antique and reproduction dolls. The excellent 74-page 8 1/2x11" book on shoes includes patterns for sandals, boots, oxfords and slippers.

MES PETITS
"MY LITTLE ONES"

(see Chapter 3)

Shortcuts to Success: The Art of Making Doll Clothes That $ell, a 17-page self-published booklet written by Diana-Marie Thorpe. She cautions dollmakers, e.g., to avoid using tiny hems, bias tape casing on the wrists of sleeves and bias tape or lace around necks.

NATIONAL CLOTH DOLL MAKERS ASSOCIATION

Judy Waters
1601 Provincetown Dr.
San Jose, CA 95129-4742
408/252-1567

Established in 1984
Information: SASE

This recently formed group plans to produce a newsletter for its members who are interested in making, collecting, selling, buying and/or reading about cloth dolls and toys. The establishment of doll clubs will be encouraged.

She Who Dies With the Most Fabric Wins.

© Osage County Quilt Factory

OSAGE COUNTY
QUILT FACTORY

(see Chapter 1)

Take It and Make It, written by Elinor Peace Bailey and Virginia Robertson, subtitled "a bizarre bazaar idea book of inexpensive projects for the car, club or at home with broken bits of time . . ."

This is a delightful how-to booklet from the zany Bailey-Robertson twosome. They admit, right up front in the brief introduction, that their designs are not always "safe and normal . . . but just a little off-beat." Among the offerings are patterns for five soft-sculpture miniatures - a Crazy Quilt Cat Family, Little Goose, The Rabbit Family, Sweet Lady Clair and Thimblena (a 9" wearable doll) - and Flat Pat, a fabric paper doll. The best thing about this booklet, however, is the "Quilter's Bored Game", sort of a Monopoly for fabric lovers. Everyone starts with five yards of fabric and proceeds to lose or take a yard around the "bored". Cards dictate who wins and who loses yardage, such as "You're guilty of wimpy stuffing and your teddies have the bends. For shame, lose a yard" and "You put dolls on your quilts and quilts on your dolls and quilts and dolls on your body and you're magnificent. Take a yard." The winner? "She Who Dies with the Most Fabric," of course!

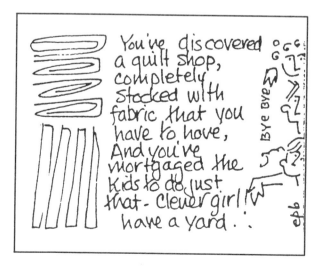

PLATYPUS PUBLICATIONS

(see Chapter 1)

The Fine Art of Stuffing Cloth Dolls, The Fine Art of Making Faces on Cloth Dolls, and *Teaching a Sock Doll Workshop*, three excellent self-published booklets written by Colette Wolff. The 16-page booklet on stuffing, first published in 1981, is a must and should be in the sewing basket of *every* cloth toy and dollmaker. "Stuffing takes its own sweet time," says Colette. "The goal is always the same. To fill out every corner and curve of the casing as far as it will expand. To make the casing as rounded as it will allow. To shape every part of the figure with stuffing on the inside and modelling from the outside. To stuff a flat casing into a 3-dimensional life."

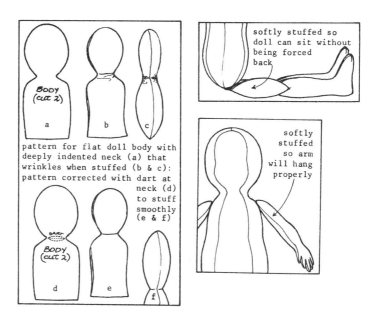

Tips from The Fine Art of Stuffing Cloth Dolls, © *Colette Wolff.*

SEW-SO-EASY

(see Chapter 1)

Guide to Making Money with Handicrafts, a 40-page self-published booklet written by Bonnie MacRae, offers lots of good tips on selling handmade dolls. "If you have a young daughter or granddaughter, always give them one of your dolls to carry when you make a trip to the grocery store," suggests Bonnie. "Have a set of cards ready with your name and address so you can take orders from the admiring mothers and grandmothers who see your dolls. You can build up quite a business this way if you are naturally friendly and have a cute child."

© Bonnie MacRae

MAKING DOLLS IN QUANTITY

At this point you may feel that the time it takes to make dolls becomes very important, because the more dolls you can make, the more you will be able to sell. Start examining your sewing methods, and looking into ways to make short cuts that do not lessen the quality of your dolls.

One real time waster is a messy or disorganized sewing area. If you don't have enough space that is just devoted to sewing, set aside a corner of a room where you can work undisturbed. Then organize everything so there is a place for everything and keep everything in its place so you can put your hand on it the minute you need it . . .

Another way to save time is to make more than one doll at a time. Each step that you take in making a doll requires that you set up your working space, and each time you put everything out you spend time. It takes time to put out your sewing machine. Thread the needle with the right color thread. Put out pins and so on. For instance when cutting, you have to set up a folding table or clear an area (5 minutes), then you have to spread out the cloth on the cutting surface (3 minutes). You have to organize, iron and layout, pin and cut (15 minutes). Then you have to put away your scissors, pins, pattern, and fold up your table and so on (10 more minutes). If you had cut out an extra 10 dolls while you had everything set up, you would have saved yourself 10 times 33 minutes, or around 5½ hours! Of course, you may work faster than this or slower, but the principle is still there. Make more than one doll at the same time and you will save time. Cut out 10 dolls of the same design. Then sew 10 dolls of the same design. Stuff them one after the other. Add the hair all at once. Finish ten little faces one after the other. All this is certainly not boring because each little doll will develop a distinct personality and it is fun to compare them as you go along.

— from *Guide to Making Money with Handicrafts,* by Bonnie MacRae, © 1982.

TAILORMAID TOGS FOR TEDDY BEARS

(see Chapter 3)

Tips on Sewing Fur, a self-published booklet.

ALICE & LEE WELPLEY

(see Chapter 1)

How to Make a Pressed Felt Doll, a 32-page self-published illustrated book.

CASTLE PRESS
PUBLICATIONS, INC.

PO Box 247
Washington, NJ 07882-0247
201/689-7512

Established in 1961

Doll Castle News, a bimonthly magazine, edited by Edwina L. Mueller, covers dollmakers and dolls in all media and was the *first* doll periodical to be established.

COLLECTOR
COMMUNICATIONS CORP.

170 5th Ave.
New York, NY 10010-5911
212/989-8700

Established in 1982

Dolls - The Collector's Magazine, a quarterly magazine edited by Krystyna Poray Goddu, is a slick full-color publication (circulation: 50,000) devoted to investment dolls, not excluding cloth dolls. The Winter 1984 issue, e.g., contains an article on contemporary Sherlock Holmes dolls as well as profiles of three studio dollmakers, including Gabriele West and REBECCA IVERSON (see Chapter 5).

COLLEEN'S COTTAGE
ENTERPRISES

Gary and Colleen Bergman
PO Box 1089
Mt. Shasta, CA 96067-1089
916/926-5009

Established in 1982
Brochure: LSASE

The Cloth Doll, a quarterly magazine edited by Colleen (a.k.a. Leta) Bergman; 60 ethnic doll and costume patterns.

The only periodical that deals exclusively with cloth dolls, Leta's folksy approach has brought her several thousand subscribers in a relatively short time. The covers and inside pages are frequently adorned with her line drawings, but the small-format magazine is packed with helpful articles and patterns contributed by doll designers who receive ads in lieu of payment. This unique "co-op" approach has been the foundation of the home-based periodical from the beginning. "We started the magazine as a co-operative venture," says Leta, "enlisting assistance from dozens of other cloth doll designers and toymakers who wrote articles, submitted patterns and shared their business advice with our readers."

That Patchwork Place

Muslin Mummies & Daddies

by Nancy Southerland-Holmes

FULL-SIZE PATTERNS INCLUDED

DAISY PUBLISHING, INC.

PO Box 67
Mukilteo, WA 98275-0067
206/347-1414

Established in 1983

Doll Crafter, a bimonthly how-to-do-it magazine (circulation: 40,000), edited by Barbara Campbell, focusing on antique and reproduction dolls.

THE HUG CORPORATION

300 E. 40th St.
New York, NY 10016-2141
212/682-HUGS

BearHugs, a monthly international publication for bear lovers, features bear artists and their work, a monthly "cover bear" sweepstakes and a popular comic-strip bear-character, the witty and wise *Hug*.

HOBBY HOUSE PRESS, INC.

900 Frederick St.
Cumberland, MD 21502-1298
301/759-3770

The Doll Reader and *The Teddy Bear and friends*, full-color magazines for doll and bear aficionados.

The Doll Reader, established in 1982 and published eight times a year, is edited by Virginia Ann Heyerdahl. *The Teddy Bear and friends*, established in 1983, is a glossy quarterly magazine edited by Albert Christian Revi.

SEELEY'S CERAMIC SERVICE, INC.

Seeley's Ceramic Service, Inc.
9 River St.
Oneonta, NY 13820-2338
607/432-4977

Established in 1977

The Doll Artisan, a bimonthly magazine edited by Eva Oscarsson, is a publication of The Doll Artisan Guild. It is primarily for reproduction dollmakers.

THE TEDDY TRIBUNE

254 W. Sidney St.
St. Paul, MN 55107-3494
612/291-7571

Established in 1980

This international publication includes news and views of the bear world, including product reviews, future events and articles on bear makers.

TOWER PRESS, INC.

PO Box 337
Seabrook, NH 03874-0337

Established in 1977

National Doll World, a full-color bimonthly magazine edited by Barbara Hall Pedersen, with emphasis on *all* dolls. *Doll Castle News*, *The Cloth Doll* and *National Doll World* are the three national periodicals that provide the best coverage of cloth dolls and their makers.

HOW-TO PATTERN
BOOKLETS

There are dozens of excellent 8 1/2"x11" how-to pattern booklets available at your local fabric and/or craft supply stores. Most are written by leading cloth doll and soft toy designers and are usually extremely good value. All feature full-color covers and step-by-step illustrations. You will recognize such names as Nancy Southerland-Holmes (TROTTER'S CREEK, Chapter 6) who has written numerous booklets, including *Muslin Mummies & Daddies*, and Nora Fran Dilks (DESIGN WORKSHOP, Chapter 1), *More Dolls to Cross-stitch & Sew*. Companies to look for include ABC NEEDLEWORK & CRAFTS PUBLICATIONS, AMERICAN SCHOOL OF NEEDLEWORK, CRAFT COURSE PUBLISHERS, PAT DEPKE BOOKS, GAYLEMOT PUBLISHING, GICK PUBLISHING, GLP INTERNATIONAL, L. P. PUBLISHING, PLAID ENTERPRISES, THAT PATCHWORK PLACE and THE VANESSA-ANN COLLECTION.

OUT-OF-PRINT BOOKS

(May be available at your library or through inter-library loan)

American Costume Dolls: How to Make and Dress Them, Nina Ralston Jordan (New York: Harcourt, Brace & Co., 1941).

The Art of Making Cloth Toys, Charlene Davis Roth (Radnor, PA: Chilton Book Co., 1974).

The Big Book of Soft Toys, Mabs Tyler (New York: McGraw-Hill Book Co., 1972).

The Craft of Stuffed Toys, Esme McLaren (London: G. Bell and Sons, Ltd., 1961).

Doll Making, Audrey Vincente Dean (Sussex: Wayland Publishers Ltd., 1978).

Doll Making: A Creative Approach, Jean Ray Laury (New York: Van Nostrand Reinhold Co., 1970).

Dolls and How to Make Them, Margaret Hutchings (London: Mills & Boon Ltd., 1963).

Dolls in National and Folk Costume, Jean Greenhowe (Newton Centre, MA: Charles T. Branford Co., 1978).

Dolls, Puppedolls, and Teddy Bears, Estelle Ansley Worrell (New York: Van Nostrand Reinhold Co., 1977).

Dressing Dolls, Charlene Davis Roth (New York: Crown Publishers, Inc., 1976).

Early North American Dollmaking, Iris Sanderson Jones (San Francisco: 101 Productions, 1976).

How to Make Upside-Down Dolls, John Coyne and Jerry Miller (New York: Bobbs-Merrill, 1977).

Introducing Soft Toy Making, Delphine Davidson (Newton Centre, MA: Charles T. Branford Co., 1969).

Making and Dressing a Rag Doll, Suzy Ives (New York: Drake Publishers, Inc., 1972).

Soft People: The Art of Dollcrafting, Loretta Pompilio (Trumansburg, NY: The Crossing Press, 1979).

Woman's Day Book of Best-Loved Toys & Dolls, Julie Houston, ed. (New York: Sedgewood Press, 1982).

BOOKS IN PRINT

(May be available at your local bookstore or library)

Adventures in Toy-Making, Gillian Bradshaw-Smith (New York: Taplinger Publishing Co., 1976).

American Folk Dolls, Wendy Lavitt (New York: Alfred A. Knopf, Inc., 1982).

Big Book of Stuffed Toy & Doll Making, Margaret Hutchings (New York: Dover Publications, 1983, originally published by Mills & Boon Ltd, London, 1959).

Cherished Dolls to Make for Fun, Better Homes & Gardens editors (Des Moines, IA: Meredith Corp., 1984).

The Collector's Encyclopedia of Cloth Dolls, Johana Gast Anderton (Lombard, IL: Wallace-Homestead Book Co., 1984).

The Complete Book of Doll Making and Collecting, Catherine Christopher (New York: Dover Publications, 1970, originally published in 1949).

Cuddly Toys and Dolls, Jean Greenhowe (New York: Sterling Publishing Co., Inc., 1983).

Dollmaker's Workshop, Vera P. Guild (New York: Hearst Books, 1981).

Dolls for Children to Make, Suzy Ives (London: B. T. Batsford Ltd., distributed by David & Charles Inc., North Pomfret, VT, 1975).

Dolls for Sale, Valerie Janitch (London: Faber & Faber Ltd., 1980).

Good Design in Soft Toys, Rudi de Sarigny (New York: Peter Smith Publishers, Inc., originally published simultaneously by Mills & Boon Ltd., London, and Taplinger Publishing Co., Inc., New York, 1971).

The How-to Book of International Dolls, Loretta Holz (New York: Crown Publishers, Inc., 1980).

Making American Folk Art Dolls, Gini Rogowski and Gene DeWeese (Radnor, PA: Chilton Book Co., 1975).

Making Collector's Dolls, Venus A. Dodge (New York: Sterling Publishing Co., Inc., 1983).

Making Mascot Dolls, Jean Greenhowe (London: B. T. Batsford Ltd., distributed by David & Charles Inc., North Pomfret, VT, 1981).

Making Your Own Teddy Bear, Peggy and Alan Bialosky (New York, Workman Publishing Co., Inc., 1982).

Soft Sculpture, Carolyn Vosburg Hall (Worcester, MA: Davis Publications, Inc., 1981).

Soft Toys to Stitch and Stuff, Jean Mandrell Benson (New York: Doubleday & Company, Inc., 1983).

Step-By-Step Dollmaking, Barbara Marsten (New York: Van Nostrand Reinhold Co., 1981).

The Splendid Soft Toy Book (New York: Sterling Publishing Co., Inc., 1981).

The Techniques of Soft Toymaking, Enid Anderson (London: B. T. Batsford Ltd., distributed by David & Charles Inc., North Pomfret, VT, 1982).

The Teddy Bear Book (New York: Arco Publishing Inc., 1984).

The Teddy Bear Craft Book, Carolyn Vosburg Hall (New York: Van Nostrand Reinhold Co., 1983).

Teddy Bears and How to Make Them, Margaret Hutchings (New York: Dover Publications, 1977, originally published by Mills & Boon Ltd., London, 1964).

The Weepeeple, Ed and Stevie Baldwin (New York: G. P. Putnam's Sons, 1983).

The Woman's Day Book of Soft Toys & Dolls, Joan Russell (New York: Simon and Schuster, 1980).

Geographical Listing of Mail Order Companies

ALABAMA	The Doll House, Rt. 17, Box 605, Cullman, AL 35055-8791
	Elf Designs, PO Box 76210, Birmingham, AL 35253-6210
	The Grizzlies, Rt. 1, Box 410, Elberta, AL 36530-9752
	Little River Crafts, PO Box 1086, Ft. Payne, AL 35967-1086
	Miss Martha Originals, PO Box 5038, Glencoe, AL 35905-0038
ALASKA	Alaska Craft, PO Box 11-1102, Anchorage, AK 99506-0011
	The Woolie Works, 6201 E. Huffman Rd., Anchorage, AK 99516-2442
ARIZONA	Bellston Originals, 3025 W. Lupine Ave., Phoenix, AZ 85029-3255
	Bettina's Doll Designs, 2509 N. Campbell Ave., Tucson, AZ 85719
	Country Kitchen Creations, 7625 W. Bluefield Ave., Peoria, AZ 85345-3117
	Kenja Designs, 139 W. Pershing Ave., Phoenix, AZ 85029-1814
	Little Pleasures, 127 E. LeMarche Ave., Phoenix, AZ 85022-2502
	Moonbeams, PO Box 36024, Phoenix, AZ 85067-6024
	Nantucket Bears, PO Box 36024, Phoenix, AZ 85067-6024
ARKANSAS	Handy Hands, Rt. 2, Box 51, Mountainburg, AR 72946-9503
	Heart's Desire, PO Box 506, Eureka Springs, AR 72632-0506
CALIFORNIA	Aardvark to Zebra, 219 El Arbol Dr., Carlsbad, CA 92008-4317
	Alice * Lee Welpley, 6485 Pleasant Valley Rd., Diamond Springs, CA 95619-9601
	Amadeus Fairy Tales, 437 San Mateo Ave., San Bruno, CA 94066-4415
	Andee's Arti-Facts, 1641 N. Maury Dr., Santa Maria, CA 93454-1635
	Animal Trax, PO Box 265, Upland, CA 91785-0265

CALIFORNIA
(continued)

Anne O'Brien Doll Millinery Supplies, 11208 Tiara St., North Hollywood, CA 91601-1232

Annemade, 953 W. 3rd St., Pomona, CA 91766-1420

Artis, Inc., PO Box 407, Solvang, CA 93463-0407

Babes & Bears, PO Box 311, North San Juan, CA 95960-0311

Bajama Originals, 1344 Montevideo St., Placentia, CA 92670-3909

Barefoot Boutique, 21205 Golondrina St., Woodland Hills, CA 91364-5809

Bear Biz, PO Box 1283, Los Gatos, CA 95031-1283

Bear Clawset, 27 Palmero Walk, Long Beach, CA 90803-4029

Bear Existence, PO Box 922, Pasadena, CA 91102-0922

Bear Necessities, PO Box 787, Mt. Shasta, CA 96067-0787

Bears & Bibs, PO Box 691, Downey, CA 90241-0691

Bears & Friends, 35106 Date, Yucaipa, CA 92399-3106

Bears 'N Toyland, 2316 Wind River Rd., El Cajon, CA 92020-8649

Bonnie Elaine Dolls, 130 E. Placer St., Auburn, CA 95603-5242

Briar House, PO Box 2066, Dublin, CA 94568-0206

Cherie's 3-D Creations, Suite 235, 10615-G Tierrasanta, San Diego, CA 92124-2605

Christopher Brown, PO Box 2628, Palm Springs, CA 92263-2628

Clones by Curran, PO Box 752, El Cerrito, CA 94530-0752

Coiffures, PO Box 490, Pine Grove, CA 95665-0490

Collee Bears, 1825 Forest Ave., Carlsbad, CA 92008-1017

Colleen's Cottage Enterprises, PO Box 1089, Mt. Shasta, CA 96067-1089

Crafty Creations, PO Box 867, Clovis, CA 93613-0867

The Cricket Factory, PO Box 213, Apple Valley, CA 92307-0061

Crosscreek, 1465 4th St., Berkeley, CA 94710-1374

Fabric Fun Patterns, PO Box 4354, Fremont, CA 94539-0435

Forget*Me*Nots, 103 W. Marshall St., San Gabriel, CA 91776-4105

Gaillorraine Originals, 407 Brentwood Dr., Tehachapi, CA 93561-2237

Guiliani Creations, PO Box 1239, Ojai, CA 93023-1239

Heart and Hand, PO Box 1124, El Torro, CA 92630-1124

Judy Jennings Ltd., PO Box 1527, Tustin, CA 92681-1527

Kountry Kreations, 19420 Stefani Ave., Cerritos, CA 90701-7124

Little Old Lady Originals, 1779 East Ave., Hayward, CA 94541-5401

Little Punkin Patterns, PO Box 1380, Woodbridge, CA 95258-1380

Lucky Star Handicrafts, 20551 Hwy. 128, Yorkville, CA 95495-9205

CALIFORNIA (continued)	Luv N' Stuff, PO Box 85, Poway, CA 92064-0001
	The Mail Pouch, PO Box 1373, Monrovia, CA 91016-1373
	Margie's Creations, 1950 Port Cardiff Place, Newport Beach, CA 92660-5415
	Marie Louise Originals, 15802 Springdale St., Huntington Beach, CA 92649-1728
	Merrily Supply Co., 8542 Ranchito Ave., Panorama City, CA 91402
	Miss Lizzi's, 2475 Coolidge Ave., #3, Oakland, CA 94601-2637
	National Cloth Doll Makers Association, 1601 Provincetown Dr., San Jose, CA 95129-4742
	The Pig Works, PO Box 1305, Woodland Hills, CA 91365-1305
	R-Renditions, PO Box 1919, Garden Grove, CA 92642-1919
	Raggedy Joan's Dolls, 10436 Midway St., Bellflower CA 90706-5048
	Rainbow Fog, 1546 Van Dyke Ave., San Francisco, CA 94124-3235
	Roda Wee Doll Patterns, 2291 W. Hearn Ave., Santa Rosa, CA 95407-7377
	Runnin' Bear Co., 6310 California St., San Francisco, CA 94121-1924
	Sew Special, 2762 Londonderry Dr., Sacramento, CA 95827-1317
	The Sewing Centipede, PO Box 218, Midway City, CA 92655-0218
	Shastabear, PO Box 384, Mt. Shasta, CA 96067-0384
	Spencer's Zoo, 715 Walnut Dr., Rio Dell, CA 95562-1426
	Springtime, 4860 Ontario Way, Santa Maria, CA 93455-5704
	Sugar Plum Bears & Co., 317 Hickory St., Napa, CA 94558-5850
	Sugar Plum Creations, PO Box 2914, Hesperia, CA 92345-1111
	Sweet Talker, PO Box 19, Lompoc, CA 93428-0019
	T.E.M. of California, PO Box 4311, Fullerton, CA 92634-4311
	Tempty Bears and Toys, 15 Fleming Ave., San Jose, CA 95127-2451
	Tomorrow's Treasures, 2836 E. Imperial Hwy., Brea, CA 92621-6714
	Vea Prints, 829 Heinz Ave., #2, Berkeley, CA 94710-2739
	Vickie Solomon, 111 S. Seminary St., Napa, CA 94559-3705
	Young Luvs, 8423 Eton Ave., Canoga Park, CA 91304-2733
COLORADO	Andi's Doll Nook, 4326 W. 4th St. Rd., Greeley, CO 80634-1342
	Clever Creations, 35581 WCR 31, Eaton, CO 80615
	D. G. Enterprises, 1005 W. Oak St., Ft. Collings, CO 80521-2408
	Golden Fun Kits, PO Box 10697, Golden, CO 80401-0600
	The Greebe Gallery, 11531 St. Paul Ct., Thornton, CO 80233-2410
	Heart Felt Friends, 2713 Dunbar Ave., Ft. Collins, CO 80526-2210

COLORADO (continued)	Heart Patches, 90 S. Wadsworth, Lakewood, CO 80226-1549
	Lorna's Bestiary, PO Box 2568, Dillon, CO 80435-2568
	Lyn's Doll House, PO Box 8341, Denver, CO 80201-8341
	Muffin & Me, 2843 Trenton Way, Fort Collins, CO 80526-2247
CONNECTICUT	Baskets & Bears, 14 Rindge Rd., Union, CT 06076-9515
	C.A.P. Designs, 5 Yellow Birch Rd., Middletown, CT 06457-4947
	Dovic Dolls, 52 Clinton Hill Rd., Wolcott, CT 06716-1011
	Fairfield Processing Corp., PO Box 1157, Danbury, CT 06810-1157
	Lucy White, PO Box 982, Westbrook, CT 06498-0982
	Pattern Plus, 21 Mountain View Ave., New Milford, CT 06776-4725
DELAWARE	Loeber Cats 84, 517 White House Beach, Millsboro, DE 19966
FLORIDA	Calico Critters, 3212 Storrington Dr., Tallahassee, FL 32308-2817
	Florida Supply House, Inc., PO Box 847, Bradenton, FL 33506-0847
	I'm Stuffed, PO Box 16853, Tampa, FL 33687-6853
	Imports by Clotilde, 237 SW 28th St., Fort Lauderdale, FL 33315-3131
	Rayna, PO Box 37, Dunedin, FL 34296-0037
	Waas Originals, 4341 NW 3rd Terrace, Pompano Beach, FL 33064-2532
	Wil-Mar Creations, PO Box 3422, Kissimmee, FL 32742-3422
GEORGIA	Atlanta Puffections, PO Box 13524, Atlanta, GA 30324-0524
	Double D Productions, Inc., 4110 Willow Ridge Rd., Douglasville, GA 30135-2750
	Hen's Nest Home of the "Blossom Babies", PO Box 99, Hiawassee, GA 30546-0099
	Made with Love, Ltd., 1832 Young Rd., Lithonia, GA 30058-5550
	San Lou, PO Box 70876, Marietta, GA 30007-0876
	Yours Truly, Inc., PO Box 80218, Atlanta, GA 30366-0218
IDAHO	Design Source, PO Box 158, Greenleaf, ID 83626-0158
	Laurie Carlson Dolls, Rt. 1, Box 75, Deary, ID 83823-9719
ILLINOIS	All-Foam Products Co., Inc., PO Box 128, Morton Grove, IL 60053-0128
	Cab's Trunk, 639 S. Quincy, Hinsdale, IL 60521-3953
	Carolee Creations, 787 Industrial Dr., Elmhurst, IL 60126-1141
	Country Cousin, PO Box 94893, Schaumburg, IL 60194-0893

ILLINOIS (continued)	Dolls by Carolean, 457 W. German, Chester, IL 62233-1324
	The Hobbie Hut, PO Box 222, Bedford Park, IL 60499-0222
	Honey Bee Dolls, 615 N. Buell Ave., Aurora, IL 60506-3524
	Kirchen Bros., PO Box C1016, Skokie, IL 60076-8016
	The People Factory, 12 Merrygrove, Jacksonville, IL 62650-1714
	Miss Perky's Patterns, 215 Summit Dr., Tower Lakes, Barrington, IL 60010-1149
	Needlecraft Corp. of America, 3900 N. Claremont Ave., Chicago, IL 60618-3887
	Taylor's Cutaways & Stuff, 2802 E. Washington St., Urbana, IL 61801-4699
	Windmill City Cradles, 220 Ellen Lane, Batavia, IL 60510-2502
INDIANA	Fanciful Daydreams, PO Box 363, Goshen, IN 46526-0363
	Gohn Bros., PO Box 111, Middlebury, IN 46540-0111
	Hunney Bears, PO Box 448, Hanover, IN 47243-0448
	Lillian's Country Charm, 2501 N. Reserve, Muncie, IN 47303-5316
	Patterns by Joan, PO Box 6103, Greenwood, IN 46142-6103
	The Teddy Bear Factory, 7007 S. Ketcham, Bloomington, IN 47401-9228
IOWA	CR's Crafts, PO Box 8, Leland, IA 50453-0008
	Wee Wonder Works, PO Box 552, Russell, IA 50238-0552
KANSAS	The Country Place, Rt. 1, Box 40, Gardner, KS 66030-9715
	Country Ritz, 1217 Moro, Manhattan, KS 66502-5352
	Cranberry Creek, PO Box 12434, Overland Park, KS 66212-0434
	Hedy Haukenberry, 317 Clay, Topeka, KS 66606-1135
	My Ty Creations, 806 Main St., Hays, KS 67601-4441
	Osage County Quilt Factory, 400 Walnut, PO Box 490, Overbrook, KS 66524-0490
KENTUCKY	Petronella Patterns, 1672 Donelwal Dr., Lexington, KY 40511-9021
LOUISIANA	Dolls by Frances, Rt. 3, Box 542, Deville, LA 71328-9803
	Love Me Dolls, PO Box 1060, Logansport, LA 71049-1060
	Teche Country, 408 Birch St., New Iberia, LA 70560-1906
	Twyla Dolls, 2618 N. 9th St., West Monroe, LA 71291-5140
MAINE	Mama Makes Em, 10 Fremont St., Machias, ME 04654-1312

MARYLAND	Buckwheats, 200 W. Padonia Rd., Timonium, MD 21093-2107
	Dinosaur, 11706 Orebaugh Ave., Wheaton, MD 20902-2865
	Hobby House Press, Inc., 900 Frederick Ave., Cumberland, MD 21502-1298
	Nancy Weik, Rt. 1, Box 148, Hebron, MD 2183-9774
	Noble Bears, Box 8662, Rockville, MD 20856-8662
	Pieces of Olde, 5614 Greenspring Ave., Baltimore, MD 21209-4308
	Pleasant Walk Folk, 11025 Pleasant Walk Rd., Myersville, MD 21773-9222

MASSACHUSETTS	Bear-In-Mind, 20 Beharrell St., Concord, MA 01742-2962
	Berman Leathercraft, Inc., 25 Melcher St., Boston, MA 02210-1599
	Carlsen Creations, 7 Parker Rd., Bedford, MA 01730
	Dolls Plus, PO Box 13, Oxford, MA 01540-0013
	The Felters Co., 22 West St., Millbury, MA 01527-2622
	Flightsong, 32 Forest Lane, Millis, MA 02054-1747
	Fluff 'N' Stuff, 150 Wareham St., Middleboro, MA 02346-2403
	M. Siegel Co., Inc., 120 Pond St., Ashland, MA 01721-2098
	Tumbleweed, 99 Mt. Auburn St., Cambridge, MA 02138-4901

MICHIGAN	Air-Lite Synthetic Mfg., Inc., 342 Irwin St., Pontiac, MI 48053-2399
	Bear Minimum, 2765 Sunnyknoll, Berkley, MI 48072-1530
	Christmas Everyday, PO Box 1173, Grand Rapids, MI 49501-1173
	The Designery, PO Box 2887, Kalamazoo, MI 49003-2887
	Divine Designs, Rt. 1, Box 1656, Grayling, MI 49738-9801
	Dixie's Love & Stuff, 2328 Vernor Rd., Lapeer, MI 48446-8315
	Dollmakers Sewing & Crafts, PO Box 4116, Flint, MI 48504-0116
	Dottie's Darlings, 203 S. Truhn Rd., Fowlerville, MI 48836-8931
	Five Fingers, Inc., 37819 Schoolcraft Ave., Livonia, MI 48150-1009
	Gene Dawes, 3209 Erie Dr., Orchard Lake, MI 48033-6016
	Honey Bee Patterns, PO Box 91, Jenison, MI 49428-0091
	Little Charmers II, 53430 Hacker Rd., Colon, MI 49040-9762
	Peaceful Kingdom, Elm Valley Rd., Buchanan, MI 49107-9530
	Peachypie Country Crafts, PO Box 1099, Bay City, MI 48706-0099
	Puffs 'N Stuffin', PO Box 333, Grandville, MI 49418-0333
	Sew What Fabrics, 2431 Eastern Ave., SE, Grand Rapids, MI 49507-3601

| MINNESOTA | Caril M. Rodine, 4708 Barbara Dr., Minnetonka, MN 55343-8702 |
| | Joy Toys, 1024 S. 2nd St., Moorhead, MN 56560-3353 |

MINNESOTA (continued)	Kurly Kuddly Kids, 1921 Juliet Ave., St. Paul, MN 55105-1710
	Teddy Bears At Home, 812 Valley Dr., Duluth, MN 55804-1745
	The Teddy Tribune, 254 W. Sidney St., St. Paul, MN 55107-3494
MISSOURI	Caroline, PO Box 289, Osage Beach, MO 65065-0289
	Classic Creations, PO Box 3882, Springfield, MO 65808-3882
	Costume Quarterly for Doll Collectors, 38 Middlesex Dr., Brentwood, MO 63144-1031
	Diversified Foam Products, 134 Branch St., St. Louis, MO 63147-3504
	Sweet Dream Carrier, PO Box 1505, Ballwin, MO 63022-1505
MONTANA	Cabin Kids, 2347 Wylie, Missoula, MT 59802-3531
NEBRASKA	Lange Doll Factory, Rt. 3, Box 73, Ord, NE 68862-9326
	Magic Threads, 2026 Ryons, Lincoln, NE 68502-3836
	Products Unlimited, Inc., 915 N. 20th, Omaha, NE 68102-4319
NEVADA	Clearly Country, Elko, NV 89801
	Gentle Creatures, 5045 Mayberry Dr., Reno, NV 89509-2133
	Julie Belosic, PO Box 100, Genoa, NV 89411-0100
	Nevada Bear Co., 230 N. Mountain View Ave., Yerington, NV 89447-2238
	Stuffit, PO Box 18432-158, Las Vegas, NV 89114
NEW HAMPSHIRE	Homey Kids, Long Pond Rd., RFD 3, Dunbarton, NH 03045-9803
	Joseph's Coat, 26 Main St., Peterborough, NH 03458-2420
	Tower Press, Inc., PO Box 337, Seabrook, NH 03874-0337
	Unique Handmade Stuffed Toys, RFD 1, Box 369, Claremont, NH 03743-9801
NEW JERSEY	At Last, PO Box 549, Holmdel, NJ 07733
	Baronchelli Dolls & Doll Patterns, 51 Windward Dr., Barnegat, NJ 08005-1853
	Bears Galore, PO Box 391, Ledgewood, NJ 07852-0391
	Castle Press Publications, Inc., PO Box 247, Washington, NJ 07882-0247
	Central Shippee, Inc., 46 Star Lake Rd., Bloomington, NJ 07403-1292
	Daisy Originals, PO Box 1136, Denville, NJ 07834-8136
	Ginny, 328 Cook Ave., Middlesex, NJ 08846-2001
	Homemade Huggables, 162 Summit Ave., Phillipsburg, NJ 08865-2453
	HuBears, 341 Westwood Dr., Woodbury, NJ 08096-3127
	Kamisha and Co., 51 Meadowbrook Rd., Randolph, NJ 07869-3808

NEW JERSEY (continued)	Karres Planning Corp., PO Box 662, Point Pleasant, NJ 08742-0662
	Prints Charming, 55 Mountain Blvd., Warren, NJ 07060-6329
	Stacy Fabrics Corp., 38 Passaic St., Wood Ridge, NJ 07075-1086
NEW MEXICO	Animal Crackers Pattern Co., 5824 Isleta Blvd., SW., Albuquerque, NM 87105-6628
	Dollcraft, PO Box 20104, Albuquerque, NM 87154-0104
	The Freed Co., PO Box 394, Albuquerque, NM 87103-0394
	Terian, PO Box 318, Albuquerque, NM 87103-0318
NEW YORK	All Dolled Up, 303 Kohr Rd., Kings Park, NY 11754-1215
	Beary Truly Yours, RD 2, Ballston Spa, NY 12020-9802
	Bicor Processing Corp., 300 Babylon Turnpike, Roosevelt, NY 11575-2148
	Bonnie Lynn Young, 314 S. Clinton Ave., Lindenhurst, NY 11757-5123
	Buffalo Batt & Felt Corp., 3307 Walden Ave., Depew, NY 14043-2396
	Buffalo Felt Products, PO Box 6692, Buffalo, NY 14240-6692
	By Diane, 1126 Ivon Ave., Endicott, NY 13760-1431
	Collector Communications Corp., 170 5th Ave., New York, NY 10010-5911
	The Crafty Teddy, Inc., 168 7th St., Brooklyn, NY 11215-3107
	Doll & Craft World, Inc., 125 8th St., Brooklyn, NY 11215-3115
	Dolls Patterns Costumes, 20 Wendover Rd., Rochester, NY 14610-2344
	Dollspart Supply Co., 5-15 49th Ave., Long Island City, NY 11101-5610
	G. Schoepfer, Inc., 138 W. 31st St., New York, NY 10001-3401
	Gutcheon Parchworks, Inc., PO Box 57, Prince Street Station, New York, NY 10012-0001
	The Hug Corporations, 300 E. 40th St., New York, NY 10016-2141
	Huggin's & Hangin's, 483 27th St., Niagara Falls, NY 14303-1953
	Lasting Treasures, Box 647, Rocky Point, NY 11778-0647
	Lehman Enterprises, Inc., RR 2, Box 399, Pound Ridge, NY 10576-9797
	Little Things, 113 Main St., Irvington, NY 10533-1737
	Lou's Doll Shop & Hospital, PO Box 118, Marathon, NY 13803-0118
	Material Memories, PO Box 39, Springville, NY 14141-0039
	Nayelli Design, 10-28 49th Ave., Long Island City, NY 11101-5628
	North Country Dolls, PO Box 175, Caroga Lake, NY 12032-0175
	Pellon Corp., 119 W. 40th St., New York, NY 10018-2505
	Platypus, Box 396, Planetarium Station, New York, NY 10024-0396
	Rando Machine Corp., The Commons, Macedon, NY 14502-0614
	Seeley's Ceramic Service, Inc., 9 River St., Oneonta, NY 13820-2338

NEW YORK (continued)	Standard Doll Co., 23-83 31st St., Long Island City, NY 11105-2809
	The Toy Works, Fiddlers Elbow Rd., Middle Falls, NY 12848
	Traditions-Contemporary Folk Crafts, RD 4, Box 191, Hudson, NY 12534-9804
NORTH CAROLINA	Dolls by Dollinger, PO Box 221, Toast, NC 27049-0221
	Ellen Turner Designs, Rt. 1, Box 156, Horse Shoe, NC 28742-9723
	Fabrications by Suzanne, 43 Fryling Ave., Concord, NC 28025-5705
	The Rag Doll, PO Box 456, Denver, NC 28037-0456
OHIO	Bayberry, PO Box 24404, Dayton, OH 45424-0404
	Bear With Me, Cathie Haverkamp, 780 Fairway Dr., Cincinnati, OH 45245-1821
	Bears and Babes, PO Box 6062, Chillicothe, OH 45601-6062
	Cappel's of Dayton, 2767 Holman St., Dayton, OH 45439-1633
	The Corner Cupboard of Zoar, PO Box 627, Zoar, OH 44697-0627
	Greenbrier's Dolls, 5563 Naiche Rd., Columbus, OH 43213-3508
	Jean's Doll Patterns, 1996 Harris, Sheffield Village, OH 44054-2630
	Kema, 4683 Everett Rd., Richfield, OH 44286
	Lucas Limited Editions, 467 N. Lincoln Ave., Salem, OH 44460-2909
	Mini-Magic, 3675 Reed Rd., Columbus, OH 43220-4826
	Peapods, PO Box 173, Uniontown, OH 44685-0173
	Polyart, 4670 Interstate Dr., Cincinnati, OH 45246-1110
	Punkinbears, Box 347067, Cleveland, OH 44234-7067
	Sew Lovables, 1003 E. 3rd St., Dover, OH 44622-1223
	The Stearns & Foster Co., Williams St., and Wyoming Ave., Cincinnati, OH 45215
	Storybook Editions, PO Box 426, Van Wert, OH 45891-0426
	Susan Homecrafts, 565 Broadway, Cleveland, OH 44146-2772
	The Welch Gang, 5475 Rt. 193, Andover, OH 44003-9735
	Willowood, PO Box 31301, Cincinnati, OH 45231-0301
OKLAHOMA	Pauliwog, Rt. 1, Box 249, Sand Springs, OK 74063-9418
OREGON	Amity Publications, 78688 Sears Rd., Cottage Grove, OR 97424-9470
	Best Friends, 1813 E. 14th St., The Dales, OR 97058-3305
	Charmaine Brewer, 23288 S. Reid Rd., Estacada, OR 97023-9418
	Dolls, PO Box 155, Oakridge, OR 97463-0155
	Dorothy Dear Old Fashioned Designs, PO Box 98, Forest Grove, OR 97116-0098

OREGON
(continued)

Elise Peeples Dolls, 3235 SE Taylor, Portland, OR 97214-4270

Fantasy Creations, PO Box 42374, Portland, OR 97242-0374

Fidy Ferrara's Doll World, Rt. 1, Box 365, Forest Grove, OR 97116-9750

For Kids Only, PO Box 1290, Coos Bay, OR 97420-0324

Little Brown House Patterns, PO Box 671, Hillsboro, OR 97123-0671

Patch Press, Inc., 4019 Oakman, S., Salem, OR 97302-2799

Pattylou, PO Box 996, Jacksonville, OR 97302-0996

Rainbow World, PO Box 608, Lebanon, OR 97355-0608

Son Rise Puppet Co., PO Box 5091, Salem, OR 97304-0091

The Toylady, PO Box 503, Dallas, OR 97338-0503

PENNSYLVANIA

Anne Beach, RD 4, Box 5234, Halifax, PA 17032-9426

Aunt Lois's Dolls, 1 Illicks Mill Rd., Bethlehem, PA 18017-3746

Boycan's Craft & Art Supplies, Mail Order Division, PO Box 897, Sharon, PA 16146-0897

Catherine Fischer, PO Box 9051, Pittsburgh, PA 15224-0051

Charlotte Larkin Creations, PO Box 3189, Easton, PA 18043-3189

Design Workshop, 85 Green Meadow Lane, Telford, PA 18968-2243

Fabric Folio, 5429 Claybourne St., Pittsburgh, PA 15232-1623

Home-Sew, Inc., Bethlehem, PA 18018

Images by Nammy, 78 Williams St., Bradford, PA 16701-1368

Kane Enterprises, RD 1, Box 398, Narvon, PA 17555-9744

Newark Dressmaker Supply, PO Box 2448, Lehigh Valley, PA 18001-2448

Nostalgia by Sybil, 1435 5th St., Natrona Heights, PA 15065-1204

Whimsey, RD 5, Box 5045, Spring Grove, PA 17362-9106

SOUTH CAROLINA

D. A. Brinkman, 154 Gordon Dr., Spartanburg, SC 29301-2923

Shari Dolls, PO Box 1863, Beaufort, SC 29901-1963

Waccamaw Linen, Hwy. 501, Myrtle Beach, SC 29577

SOUTH DAKOTA

Curious Characters, Ltd., 2609 S. Blauvelt, Sioux Falls, SC 57105-5118

Prairie Partner Designs, PO Box 791, Brookings, SD 57006-0791

TENNESSEE

The Carriage House, 1115 W. Outer Dr., Oak Ridge, TN 37830-8612

The Country Cottage, 1112 Coile Lane, Knoxville, TN 37922-5903

Debbie's Dolls, Rt. 1, Box 843, Atoka, TN 38004-9801

Diane's Dolls, 2112 Jenkins Rd., Chattanooga, TN 37421-2719

Mary Wootton Original Dolls, 1416 Fairridge Dr., Kingsport, TN 37664-2011

TENNESSEE	Unicorn Studios, PO Box 370, Seymour, TN 37865-0370
TEXAS	The Bee Lee Company, PO Box 36108, Dallas, TX 75235-1108
	Cat's Whiskers, 113 Kenway, Rockwell, TX 75087-3535
	Crafts Unlimited, 1633 Babcock #233, San Antonio, TX 78229-4725
	Family Tree Bears, 3502 Rolling Terrace Dr., Spring, TX 77388-5146
	Ferguson Rabbitry, Rt. 1, Box 49, Anna, TX 75003-9704
	Frivals N Friends, Inc., PO Box 801101, Dallas, TX 75380-1101
	KC Creations, 748 Londonderry, El Paso, TX 79907-4718
	Stitch 'N Stuff, 4900 Winthrop West, Fort Worth, TX 76116-8287
	Threefold Cord Creations, PO Box 7463, Tyler, TX 75711-7463
UTAH	All Cooped Up Patterns, 450 N. University Ave., #204, Provo, UT 84601-2860
	Caren's Crafts, 2560 Sundown Ave., Salt Lake City, UT 84121-3228
	Chest Chums, 2436 Laguna Dr., West Jordan, UT 84084-4626
	The Eyelet and Lace Co., PO Box 15513, Salt Lake City, UT 84115-0513
	Fabric Fabrications, PO Box 81173, Salt Lake City, UT 84108-4173
	Hayseeds, 1120 E. 300 N., Pleasant Grove, UT 84062-2547
	Kalico Kastle, 45 N. Lone Peak Dr., Alpine, UT 84003
	The Pattern Place, 856 E. 275 South, Payson, UT 84651-2320
	Sew 'N Tale, 701 University Village, Salt Lake City, UT 84108-1022
	Sunny Side Up, PO Box 936, Provo, UT 84603-0936
	Woogams Originals, PO Box 68, Centerville, UT 84014-0068
VERMONT	The Vermont Country Store, Weston, VT 05161
VIRGINIA	Clearbrook Woolen Shop, PO Box 8, Clearbrook, VA 22624-0008
	Connie's Cuties, Inc., 2414 Heutte Dr., Norfolk, VA 23518-4532
	Dillon's Dolls, PO Box 2478, Newport News, VA 23602-0478
	Dimple Dolls by Georgia, PO Box 64850, Virginia Beach, VA 23464-0850
	Dixie's Dolls & Things, 6216 Thornwood Dr., Alexandria, VA 22310-2616
	Dolls By Angie, 10013 Manordale Rd., Chesterfield, VA 23832-3724
	Junko Matsubara Liesfeld, Rt. W, Box 175-C, Montpelier, VA 23192-9802
	Noisy Crow Artisans, 99 Beechwood Hills, Newport News, VA 23602-2413
	Sew-So-Easy, PO Box 736, Churchville, VA 24421-0736
WASHINGTON	Bears & Bunnies, 409 Main St., Edmonds, WA 98020-3137
	Cartier Bear Company, PO Box 1110, Camas, WA 98607-0110

WASHINGTON (continued)	Daisy Publishing, Inc., PO Box 67, Mukilteo, WA 98275-0067
	Fairy Tale Bears, 1055 Fir Park Lane, Fircrest, WA 98466-5940
	Gabriele's Doll Studios, PO Box F195-91, Blaine, WA 98230
	Judi's Dolls, PO Box 607, Port Orchard, WA 98366-0607
	Kea's Kloth, PO Box 480, Port Orchard, WA 96366-0480
	Mes Petits — "My Little Ones", PO Box 6746, Kennewick, WA 99336-0640
	M.O.R. Enterprise, 12614 NE 140th, Kirkland, WA 98034-1523
	Ms. G's Softworks, 8436 42nd SW, Seattle, WA 98136-2361
	Pioneer Sheepskin Co., PO Box 1366, Shelton, WA 98584-0916
	Rossco, PO Box 74, Auburn, WA 98071-0074
	Savage's Beasts, 146 N. 81st St., Seattle, WA 98103-4204
	Tailormaid Togs for Teddy Bears, 4037 161st St., SE, Bellevue, WA 98006-1860
	That Patchwork Place, Inc., PO Box 118, Bothell, WA 98041-0118
	Trotter's Creek, 910 13th St., Snohomish, WA 98290-1842
	Verlene's, PO Box 6113, Spokane, WA 99207-0902
	Wainwright Bears, PO Box 471, Langley, WA 98260-0471
	Waverly Lynn, PO Box 762, Coupeville, WA 98239-0762
WISCONSIN	Camille Designs, 517 S. Milwaukee St., Theresa, WI 53091
	Cottage Creations, PO Box 108, Cottage Grove, WI 53527-0108
	Little Lotus, 302 Spring St., Cambridge, WI 53523-9219
	Plumpet, 6521 S. 18th St., Milwaukee, WI 53221-5210
	Putman Co., Inc., PO Box 310, Walworth, WI 53184-0310
	Raspberry Hill Patchworks, 2277 Edge Wood Dr., Grafton, WI 53024-9637
	Rebecca Iverson * Needlesmith, Rt. 1, Box 60, Amery, WI 54001-9738
	Rosemary G. Curtius, 240 Clinton St., North Fond du Lac, WI 54935-1128
	Tiny Town Toys, PO Box 115, Cazenovia, WI 53924-0115
WYOMING	Alice's Dolls, PO Box 176, Gillette, WY 82716-0017
CANADA	Leighcraft, 819 Princess Ave., London, ON, Canada N5W 3M5
	Laddies & Lassies, RR 2, Box 230, Morden, MB, Canada R0G 1J0
	Midisland Cloth Doll Boutique, 18 Gillespie St., Nanaimo, BC, Canada V9R 4Y3

INDEX